IMPACT
CALIFORNIA SOCIAL STUDIES

California
A Changing State

INQUIRY JOURNAL

Mc
Graw
Hill
Education

Program Authors

James Banks, Ph.D.
Kerry and Linda Killinger Endowed Chair
in Diversity Studies
Director, Center for Multicultural Education
University of Washington
Seattle, Washington

Kevin P. Colleary, Ed.D.
Curriculum and Teaching Department
Graduate School of Education
Fordham University
New York, New York

William Deverell, Ph.D.
Director of the Huntington-USC Institute
on California and the West
Professor of History, University
of Southern California
Los Angeles, California

Daniel Lewis, Ph.D.
Dibner Senior Curator
The Huntington Library
Los Angeles, California

Elizabeth Logan Ph.D., J.D.
Associate Director of the Huntington-
USC Institute on California and the West
Los Angeles, California

Walter C. Parker, Ph.D.
Professor of Social Studies Education
Adjunct Professor of Political Science
University of Washington
Seattle, Washington

Emily M. Schell, Ed.D.
Professor, Teacher Education
San Diego State University
San Diego, California

mheducation.com/prek-12

Send all inquiries to:
McGraw-Hill Education
303 East Wacker Drive, Suite 2000
Chicago, IL 60601

ISBN: 978-0-07-899390-9
MHID: 0-07-899390-3

Printed in the United States of America.

3 4 5 6 7 8 9 LWI 22 21 20 19 18

Letter from the Authors

Dear Social Studies Detective,

Think about your state today. Then imagine the area that is now California long, long ago. Why did different groups of people decide to settle in California? What were their experiences like when they settled in the state? In this book, you will find out more about the rich and interesting history of California. You will see first-hand how California became a state—and how the state grew!

As you read, take on the role of a detective. You may have questions. Write them down and then analyze the text to find the answers. Take notes—write down what interests you! You can use your notes to share the excitement of California's history. Look closely—photos of real people and real places will bring this topic to life. Study the maps and read the time lines to see the changes that took California from region to state.

Enjoy your investigation into the world of social studies where you will find out how people came together to create a diverse and exciting state. How will you become a responsible and involved citizen of California? Read on for some ideas!

Sincerely,
The IMPACT Social Studies Authors

Avalon Harbor, Catalina Island, California

Contents

Reference Sources

Chapter 1

California's Geography and Early Peoples

How Did California's Geography Influence the Lives of People Long Ago?

(bkgds)McGraw-Hill Education

Chapter 2

A Spanish Colony in California

What Changes Did Spanish Explorers Bring to California?

Chapter 3

Mexican California

How Did California Change During the Period of Mexican Rule?

The Golden State

ESSENTIAL EQ QUESTION

What Early Events and People Defined the State of California?

Chapter 5

A Growing State

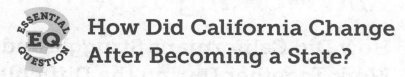

How Did California Change After Becoming a State?

Chapter 6

Californians, Struggling and Working Together

ESSENTIAL EQ QUESTION How Did Californians Struggle and Work Together During the Difficulties of the 20th Century?

(bkgds)McGraw-Hill Education

Chapter 7

California in the Modern Era

 How Has California Become an Economic and Cultural Leader Since the 1950s?

(bkgds)McGraw-Hill Education

Chapter 8

The People and Structures That Make California Work

How Do California's People and Government Help the State Thrive?

Skills and Features

Inquiry and Analysis Skills

Reader's Theater

My Notes

_____

_____

_____

_____

_____

_____

_____

_____

_____

Getting Started

You have two social studies books that you will use together to explore and analyze important social studies issues.

The Inquiry Journal

is your reporter's notebook where you will ask questions, analyze sources, and record information.

The Research Companion

is where you'll read nonfiction and literature selections, examine primary source materials, and look for answers to your questions.

Every Chapter

Chapter opener pages help you see the big picture. Each chapter begins with an **Essential Question**. This **EQ** guides research and inquiry.

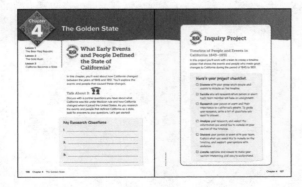

In the **Inquiry Journal,** you'll talk about the **EQ** and find out about the EQ Inquiry Project for the chapter.

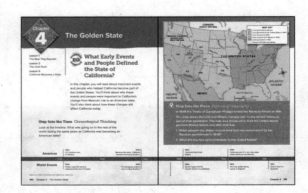

In the **Research Companion**, you'll explore the **EQ** and use a time line and map to establish the lesson's time and place.

Explore Words

Find out what you know about the chapter's academic vocabulary.

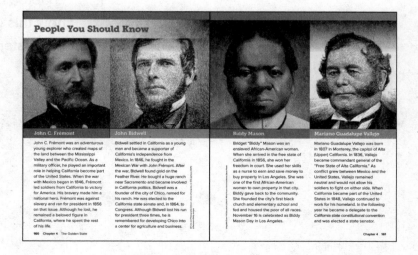

Connect Through Literature

Explore the chapter topic through fiction, informational text, and poetry.

People You Should Know

Learn about the lives of people who have made an impact in history.

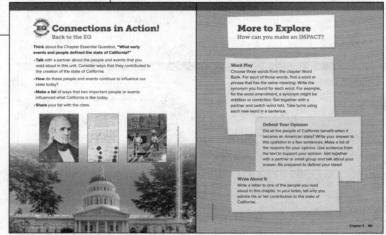

Take Action

Present your Inquiry Project to your class and assess your work with the project rubric. Then take time to reflect on your work.

Connections in Action

Think about the people, places, and events you read about in the chapter. Discuss with a partner how this gives you a deeper understanding of the EQ.

Every Lesson

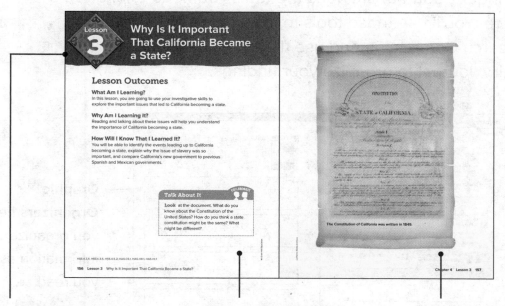

Lesson Question lets you think about how the lesson connects to the chapter EQ.

Lesson Outcomes help you think about what you will be learning and how it applies to the EQ.

Images and text provide opportunities to explore the lesson topic.

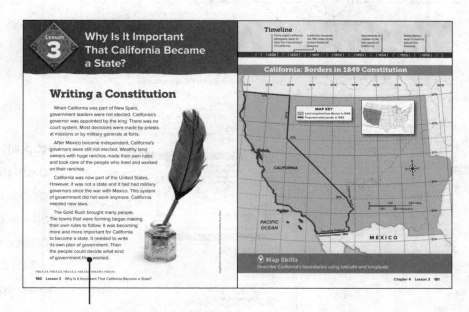

Lesson selections deepen your understanding of the lesson topic and its connection to the EQ.

Analyze and Inquire

The Inquiry Journal provides the tools you need to analyze a source. You'll use those tools to investigate the texts in the Research Companion and use the graphic organizer in the Inquiry Journal to organize your findings.

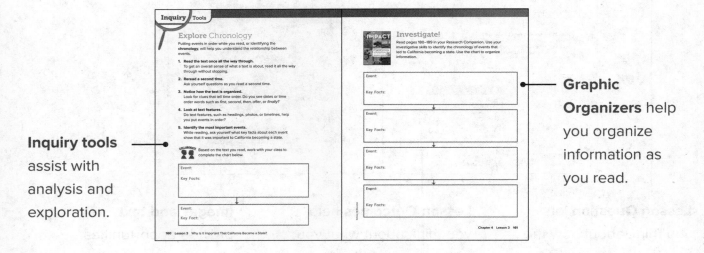

Inquiry tools assist with analysis and exploration.

Graphic Organizers help you organize information as you read.

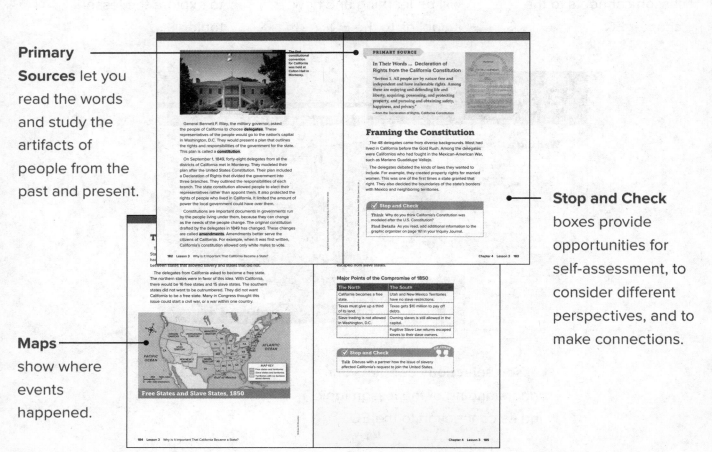

Primary Sources let you read the words and study the artifacts of people from the past and present.

Stop and Check boxes provide opportunities for self-assessment, to consider different perspectives, and to make connections.

Maps show where events happened.

Report Your Findings

At the end of each lesson you have an opportunity in the Inquiry Journal to report your findings and connect back to the EQ. In the Research Companion, you'll reconsider the lesson focus question based on what you've learned.

Think about what you have learned.

Write about it using text evidence to support your ideas.

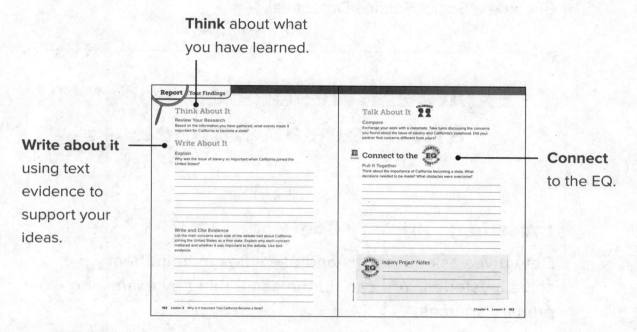

Connect to the EQ.

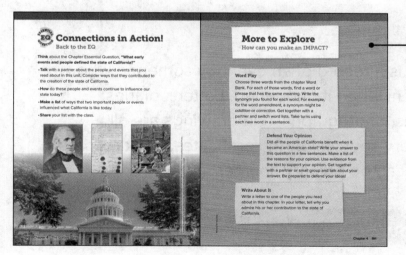

Think about what you read in the lesson. How does this give you a new understanding about the lesson focus question?

McGraw-Hill Education

Be a Social Studies Detective

How do you learn about people, places, and events in the present or in the past and the impact they had on history? Become a Social Studies Detective!

Explore, investigate, report, and make an impact!

Investigate Primary Sources

Detectives ask questions and use clues to help them solve mysteries. You can do the same thing by examining primary sources.

What's a Primary Source?

A **primary source** is a record of an event by someone who was present at the event when it happened. Letters, diaries, newspaper articles, photographs, and drawings are all examples of primary sources. Birth certificates, bank records, and even clothes can be primary sources.

Did You Know?

A **secondary source** is information from someone who was not present at the event he or she is describing. Secondary sources are based on primary sources.

Use the Detective Strategies below as you study this photo and the stamp at the right.

Social Studies Detective Strategies

Inspect

- Look closely at the source.
- Who or what is it?
- How would you describe it?

Find Evidence

- Where did the event take place?
- When did it happen?
- What are the most important details?

Make Connections

- Is this source like others you found?
- Are there other perspectives that you need to consider?
- What information supports your idea?

Social Studies Detectives examine primary sources to make connections. These connections help them learn about the past and understand the present. Use the Social Studies Detective Strategy to analyze the image below.

PRIMARY SOURCE

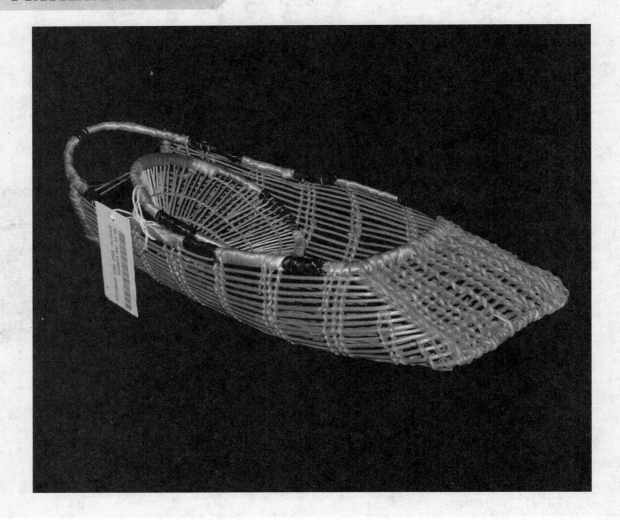

Social Studies Detective Strategy

1. Inspect
2. Find Evidence
3. Make Connections

Inspect the primary source below. Ask questions. Who wrote the diary? When do you think it was written? Why do you think it was written? Look for clues to answer your questions.

June 3d, Sunday. We left El Paso at eight this morning, and rode until ten, when we reached a deserted rancho, and with some trouble encamped near a river bed with waterholes along it. A beautiful lagoon with water holes a hundred yards long enabled us all to take refreshing baths, and I watched with pleasure the languid flight of the great blue heron, changing his position as he was approached. Two Mexicans, hunting cattle, came to us here, and Lieut. Browning bought a wild mule, for which he gave a few dollars and a broken down mule. (p.94)

September 2d. Two days out from Ures we came to some Pimos Indians washing gold from black ore, which they said produced well; we found some lumps of ore in the dust, all of irregular shapes. The value is only about one real (about ten cents) for each bushel of dirt. Each man made about two dollars a day.
We had fine grass and pond water here, and are off for Altar. (P.143)

from *Audubon's Western Journal: 1849-1850*

Explore Geography

Geographers are detectives who understand how our world is connected by studying the earth's surface and digging for clues about how people have shaped our planet. This section gives you the tools that you'll need as you explore geography.

Reading a Map

Maps are drawings of places on Earth. Most maps have standard features to help you read the map.

Map Title The map title tells you what information is on the map.

Inset Map An inset map is a small map included on a larger map. The inset map might show an area that is too large, too small, or too far away to be included on the main map.

Boundary Lines Boundary lines are political. The boundaries between states usually are drawn differently from the boundaries between nations.

Locator A locator map is a small map set into the main map. It shows the area of the map in a larger region.

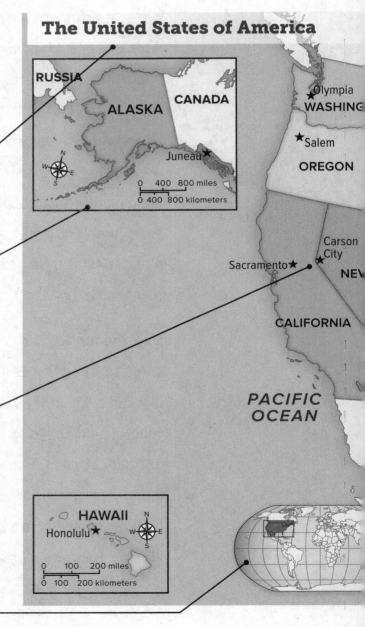

The United States of America

RUSSIA

CANADA

ALASKA

Juneau

0   400   800 miles
0   400   800 kilometers

Olympia
WASHING

Salem

OREGON

Carson
City

Sacramento

NEV

CALIFORNIA

PACIFIC
OCEAN

HAWAII

Honolulu

0   100   200 miles
0   100   200 kilometers

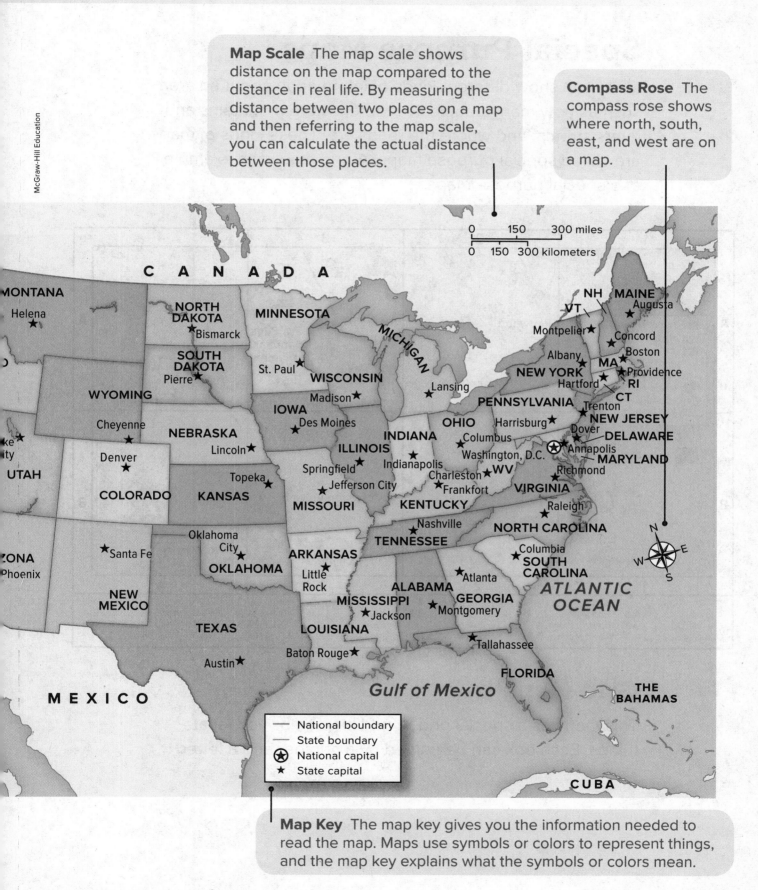

Map Scale The map scale shows distance on the map compared to the distance in real life. By measuring the distance between two places on a map and then referring to the map scale, you can calculate the actual distance between those places.

Compass Rose The compass rose shows where north, south, east, and west are on a map.

0   150   300 miles
0   150   300 kilometers

CANADA

MONTANA
Helena ★

NORTH DAKOTA
★ Bismarck

MINNESOTA

MICHIGAN

NH   MAINE
        ★ Augusta
VT
Montpelier ★   Concord
                        ★
Albany   MA   ★ Boston
★   ★ Providence
Hartford   RI

SOUTH DAKOTA
Pierre ★

St. Paul ★

WISCONSIN
Madison ★
Lansing
★

NEW YORK

WYOMING

IOWA
Des Moines ★

PENNSYLVANIA
Harrisburg ★

CT
Trenton ★
NEW JERSEY
Dover ★
★ DELAWARE
Annapolis
★ MARYLAND

Cheyenne
★

NEBRASKA
Lincoln ★

OHIO
Columbus ★

INDIANA
Indianapolis ★

ke
ity ★

Denver
★

UTAH

COLORADO

KANSAS
Topeka ★

ILLINOIS
Springfield ★

Jefferson City ★

MISSOURI

Charleston ★ WV

Washington, D.C. ⊛

Richmond ★
VIRGINIA

KENTUCKY
Frankfort ★

Raleigh ★

ZONA
Phoenix

★ Santa Fe

Oklahoma City ★

OKLAHOMA

ARKANSAS
Little Rock ★

Nashville ★
TENNESSEE

NORTH CAROLINA

Columbia
★ SOUTH CAROLINA

NEW MEXICO

TEXAS

LOUISIANA

MISSISSIPPI
Jackson ★

ALABAMA
Montgomery ★

GEORGIA
Atlanta ★

ATLANTIC OCEAN

Austin ★

Baton Rouge ★

Tallahassee ★

FLORIDA

THE BAHAMAS

MEXICO

Gulf of Mexico

CUBA

N
W   E
S

── National boundary
── State boundary
⊛ National capital
★ State capital

Map Key The map key gives you the information needed to read the map. Maps use symbols or colors to represent things, and the map key explains what the symbols or colors mean.

13a

Special Purpose Maps

Maps can show different kinds of information about an area such as how many people live there, where mountains and rivers stretch, and where the roads are. These kinds of maps are called special purpose maps. A grid map is an example of a special purpose maps.

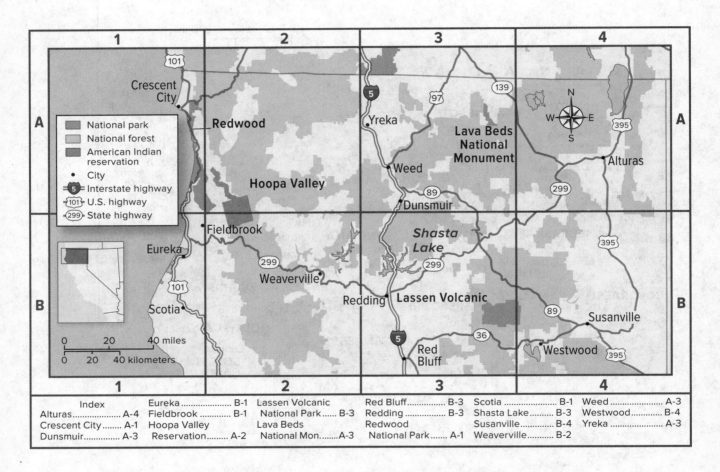

Grid Maps

This map has a special grid. A grid map helps you locate things. Each box can be named by a number and a letter.

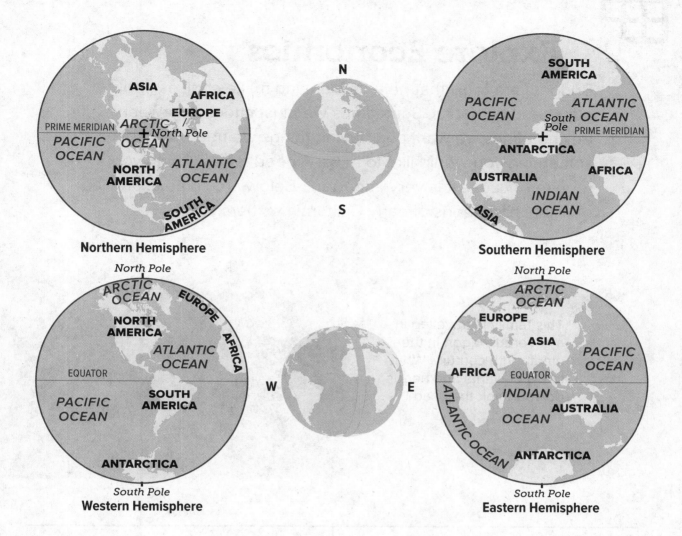

Northern Hemisphere

Southern Hemisphere

Western Hemisphere

Eastern Hemisphere

Looking At Earth

Another way to look at the earth is by using a globe.
Geographers have divided the Earth into northern and southern
hemispheres at the Equator. The area north of the Equator is
called the Northern Hemisphere. The area south of the Equator
is called the Southern Hemisphere. The Prime Meridian runs
from north to south around the Earth. The hemisphere east of
the Prime Meridian is the Eastern Hemisphere. The hemisphere
west of the Prime Meridian is the Western Hemisphere.

Explore Economics

Budgets are tools that help us plan and make choices about our spending habits. Sometimes we must choose between buying things we want and buying things we need. A want is something you would like to have. A need is something you require because it is very important. Below are some examples of wants and needs of early California settlers.

This family is traveling in a covered wagon in the nineteenth century. What kinds of wants and needs do you think they had?

Wants	Needs
toys books china plates	

Talk About It

Look closely at the picture below. How does this shopkeeper meet the wants and needs of people living in the area? Make a connection. Do we have similar wants and needs today?

PRIMARY SOURCE

An early twentieth-century grocery store

Explore Citizenship

You can learn to make an impact by being a good citizen. Some important words that define what it means to be a good citizen are listed on the following page. They help us understand how to be better citizens in our home, neighborhood, school, community, country, and world.

Take Action!

You have learned to be a Social Studies Detective by digging for clues, and you practiced exploring and investigating geography, economics, and civics. Now it's time to explore the lessons in this book and make an impact!

Suffragettes march in Washington, D.C. in 1913.

Be a Good Citizen

COURAGE
Being brave in the face of difficulty

FREEDOM
Making choices and holding beliefs of one's own

HONESTY
Telling the truth

JUSTICE
Working toward fair treatment for everyone

LEADERSHIP
Showing good behavior worth following through example

LOYALTY
Showing support for people and one's country

RESPECT
Treating others as you would like to be treated

RESPONSIBILITY
Being worthy of trust

Chapter 1

California's Geography and Early Peoples

ESSENTIAL EQ QUESTION

How Did California's Geography Influence the Lives of People Long Ago?

In this chapter, you'll learn how to use latitude and longitude to find places on maps and globes. You'll also study the geography of California. You'll examine how geography shaped the lives of California's early peoples.

COLLABORATE

Talk About It

Discuss with a partner questions you have about California's geography and its early peoples. As you research California's early history, look for answers to your questions. Let's get started!

My Research Questions

1. _____

_____

2. _____

_____

3. _____

_____

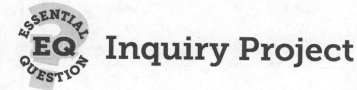

Inquiry Project

How Did Geography Affect the Settlement, Lives, and Interactions of California's Early Peoples?

You and a group of your classmates will prepare an oral presentation based on this question. You'll first form a statement to answer the question. Then you'll collect facts and details as supporting evidence. Based upon this evidence, you'll evaluate and revise the statement you formed. You and your group will then deliver an oral presentation. In your presentation, you will provide supporting evidence and helpful visuals, such as maps, time lines, and pictures.

Here's your project checklist.

☐ **Write** a statement that tells how geography affected California's early peoples.

☐ **Research** the question to collect supporting facts and details as evidence.

☐ **Evaluate** the statement you wrote and revise it, if necessary.

☐ **Prepare** a group oral presentation in which each member takes responsibility for part of the presentation.

Explore Words

Complete this chapter's Word Rater.
Write notes as you learn more about each word.

adapt

☐ Know It!
☐ Heard It!
☐ Don't Know It!

My Notes

_____

_____

_____

agriculture

☐ Know It!
☐ Heard It!
☐ Don't Know It!

My Notes

_____

_____

_____

artifact

☐ Know It!
☐ Heard It!
☐ Don't Know It!

My Notes

_____

_____

_____

expedition

☐ Know It!
☐ Heard It!
☐ Don't Know It!

My Notes

_____

_____

_____

hemispheres

☐ Know It!
☐ Heard It!
☐ Don't Know It!

My Notes

_____

_____

_____

irrigation

☐ Know It!
☐ Heard It!
☐ Don't Know It!

My Notes
_____
_____
_____

latitude

☐ Know It!
☐ Heard It!
☐ Don't Know It!

My Notes
_____
_____
_____

longitude

☐ Know It!
☐ Heard It!
☐ Don't Know It!

My Notes
_____
_____
_____

migrate

☐ Know It!
☐ Heard It!
☐ Don't Know It!

My Notes
_____
_____
_____

plateau

☐ Know It!
☐ Heard It!
☐ Don't Know It!

My Notes
_____
_____
_____

Where in the World Is California?

Lesson Outcomes

What Am I Learning?

In this lesson, you're going to use your investigative skills to identify important features of maps and globes and to use map skills to locate California.

Why Am I Learning It?

Reading and talking about map skills will help you learn more about the location and features of California.

How Will I Know That I Learned It?

You will be able to recognize globes and maps as representations of Earth, identify map features, and use map skills to locate California and identify places in California and on Earth.

Talk About It

Look at the image. What part of Earth does it show? How do you know? What features do you recognize in the image?

a satellite image of Earth from NASA

1 Inspect

Look Inspect the map and read the text. What do you think it shows?

- **Circle** details in the map that help you understand how to use it.

- **Identify** clues that tell you:

    How are the lines of latitude and longitude used?

    What features of the area in the map are labeled?

    How are directions in the map shown?

My Notes

_____

_____

_____

Pointing It Out with Latitude and Longitude

This is a map of North America. It shows lines of **latitude** and **longitude**. Latitude lines run side to side. Longitude lines run top to bottom. These lines are universal, which means they are the same on every map.

To identify an exact location on the map, find the point where the two lines meet, or intersect. You can name this point with a set of numbers called coordinates. The latitude line is written first. Then the longitude line is written second. We write the numbers in degrees, using the ° symbol.

As an example, look for the point where the 30° line of latitude intersects the 90° line of longitude. What city is labeled near that coordinate? The coordinates for New Orleans are written as 30°N, 90°W. Using coordinates is one way to find the exact location of a place on a map.

2 Find Evidence

Look Again Why do you think latitude and longitude have been helpful to navigators?

Highlight the lines of latitude and longitude that pass through California.

3 Make Connections

Talk How can you use latitude and longitude to identify a specific location? Find Los Angeles, California, on the map. How would you describe the exact location of Los Angeles, using coordinates?

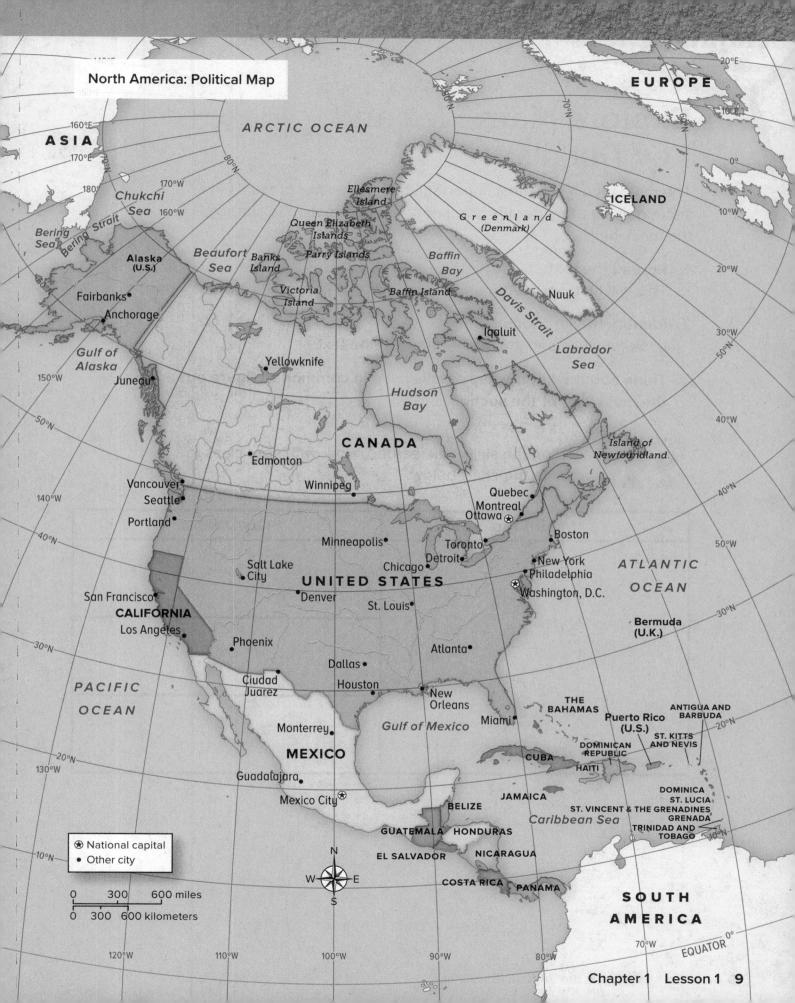

North America: Political Map

ASIA

ARCTIC OCEAN

EUROPE

ICELAND

Chukchi Sea

Bering Sea

Bering Strait

Ellesmere Island

Greenland (Denmark)

Beaufort Sea

Queen Elizabeth Islands

Banks Island

Parry Islands

Baffin Bay

Alaska (U.S.)

Fairbanks

Anchorage

Victoria Island

Baffin Island

Nuuk

Gulf of Alaska

Juneau

Yellowknife

Iqaluit

Davis Strait

Labrador Sea

CANADA

Hudson Bay

Island of Newfoundland

Edmonton

Vancouver

Seattle

Portland

Winnipeg

Quebec

Montreal

Ottawa ✪

Boston

Minneapolis

Toronto

Detroit

New York

Philadelphia

ATLANTIC OCEAN

Salt Lake City

Chicago

UNITED STATES

Washington, D.C. ✪

Denver

St. Louis

San Francisco

CALIFORNIA

Los Angeles

Phoenix

Atlanta

Bermuda (U.K.)

PACIFIC OCEAN

Ciudad Juarez

Dallas

Houston

New Orleans

Monterrey

Gulf of Mexico

Miami

THE BAHAMAS

Puerto Rico (U.S.)

ANTIGUA AND BARBUDA

MEXICO

Guadalajara

CUBA

DOMINICAN REPUBLIC

HAITI

ST. KITTS AND NEVIS

Mexico City ✪

JAMAICA

BELIZE

DOMINICA

ST. LUCIA

GUATEMALA

HONDURAS

ST. VINCENT & THE GRENADINES

GRENADA

Caribbean Sea

TRINIDAD AND TOBAGO

EL SALVADOR

NICARAGUA

COSTA RICA

PANAMA

SOUTH AMERICA

EQUATOR

✪ National capital
• Other city

0   300   600 miles

0   300   600 kilometers

N W E S

Explore Main Idea and Key Details

The **main idea** is the most important idea the author presents in a section of text. **Key details** give important information to support the main idea.

1. **Reread the text.**
   This will help you better understand what ideas are presented.

2. **Identify the key details.**
   Look for clues and important details in the text.

3. **Think about what the key details have in common to figure out the main idea of the section.**

 COLLABORATE   Based on the skills you learned, work with your class to complete the chart below.

Main Idea	Key Details

Investigate!

Read pages 8–15 in your Resea[rch] investigative skills to identify m[...] map and globe skills that help you to know where California is located in the world. Use the chart to organize information.

Main Idea	Key Details

Main Idea	Key Details

Think About It

Sum Up
Review your research. Based on the information you have gathered, how would you describe where California is located in the world?

Write About It

Describe
Write a description telling where California is located in the world.

_____

_____

_____

_____

_____

Write and Cite Evidence
Where is California located in the world? List key details about the location of California.

_____

_____

_____

_____

_____

_____

_____

_____

_____

Talk About It

Explain
Share your response with a partner. Take turns discussing how map and globe skills can help you determine the location of California and other places within the state.

Geography

Connect to the

Pull It Together
Think about the map and globe skills you learned in this lesson. How do these skills help you understand the physical features of California's geography?

_____
_____
_____
_____
_____
_____
_____
_____
_____
_____

Inquiry Project Notes

_____
_____
_____
_____
_____

Lesson Outcomes

What Am I Learning?

In this lesson, you're going to use your investigative skills to learn about landforms, regions, climate, and natural resources that make California geography unique.

Why Am I Learning It?

Reading and talking about California geography will help you understand what makes the state unique.

How Will I Know That I Learned It?

You will be able to identify the geographic features and natural resources of the state.

> **COLLABORATE**
>
> **Talk About It**
>
> **Look** closely at the pictures. What landforms can you see? How would you describe the shape of each landform?

HSS.4.1.3, HSS.4.1.4, HAS.CS.4, HAS. CS.5

Mammoth Lakes in California

Coast of California near Big Sur

Physical Map of California

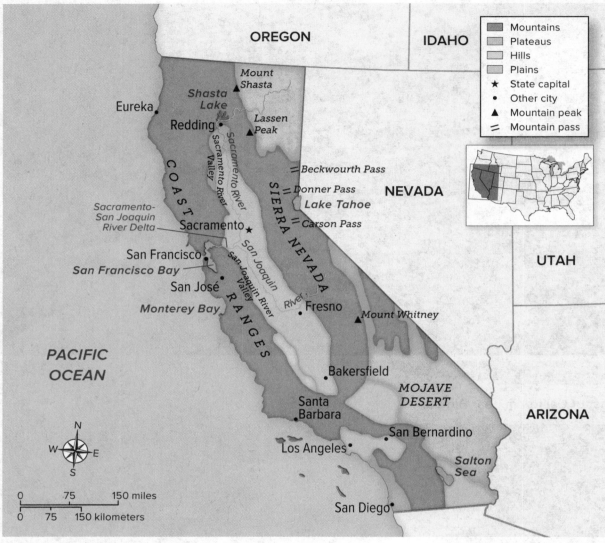

California: Landform Map

1 Inspect

Look at the landform map.

- **Circle** the landforms.
- **Discuss** with a partner where on the map the most mountains are found. Talk about the location of the mountain passes.

My Notes

_____

_____

_____

_____

Geographic features include landforms. You can use a landform map to investigate the physical features of Earth in an area. Use the map's key to identify important California landforms.

Over thousands of years, people from all over the world have been attracted to the resources produced in California. The state's land is incredibly varied. It includes mountain ranges and passes, coastal bays and natural harbors, expansive river valleys, and delta regions.

These physical features are called landforms. They are a type of geographical feature that does not include water. Naturally formed, landforms are recognizable by their appearance.

The landforms present in the state help shape how Californians live. The landforms help people decide where to live in the state and the type of home in which to live. Landforms also help determine what **agriculture** or crops will grow in the state.

- **Delta:** an area of land where a river divides into smaller waterways
- **River valley:** a large area of land drained or irrigated by a river
- **Hill:** land that is higher than the surrounding land
- **Mountain pass:** a route through a mountain range
- **Mountain range:** a line of connected mountains
- **Plain:** large area of flat or nearly flat land
- **Plateau:** extensive area of flat upland usually bounded by steep slopes on all sides
- **Valley:** a low area of land between mountains or hills

2 Find Evidence

Look Again Landform maps can provide clues about the climate of a place.

Look at the map and the descriptions of the California landforms. What landforms have water nearby? What landform is dry?

3 Make Connections

Talk Discuss and compare with a partner the physical features of each landform.

COLLABORATE

Explore Main Idea and Details

The **main idea** is the most important point the author presents. The **details** are the key points that support the main idea. To find the main idea:

1. **Look at the map once and read all the text.**
   This will help you understand what the map and text are about.

2. **Look again at the map and pay attention to all the symbols and labels.**
   Do the symbols and labels help you understand the text?

3. **Reread the text.**
   Look for information that supports the main idea. Is there a connection between the map and the text?

4. **Ask yourself, "What is important about California geography?"**
   Does the map support what you read?

COLLABORATE Based on the maps you analyzed and the text you read, work with your class to complete the chart below.

Main Idea

↓

Detail

Investigate!

Read pages 16–25 in your Research Companion. Use your investigative skills to look for text evidence that provides details to support the main idea. This chart will help you organize your notes.

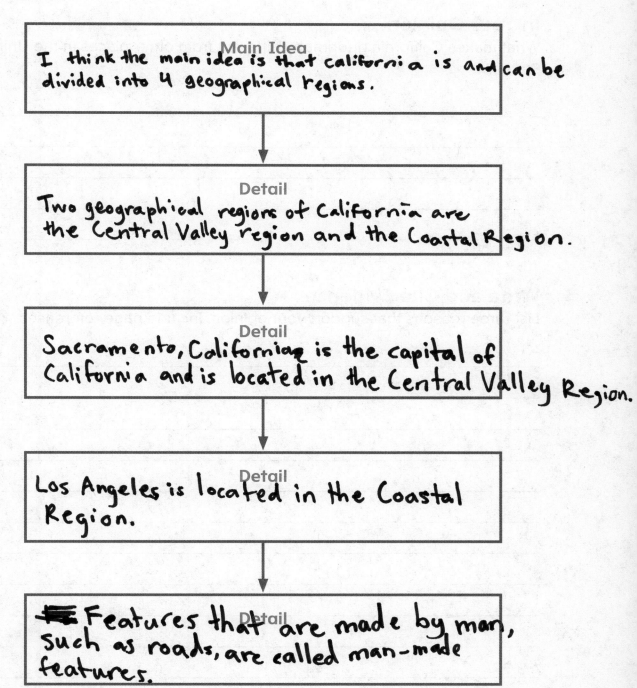

Main Idea

I think the main idea is that california is and can be divided into 4 geographical regions.

Detail

Two geographical regions of California are the Central Valley region and the Coastal Region.

Detail

Sacramento, California is the capital of California and is located in the Central Valley Region.

Detail

Los Angeles is located in the Coastal Region.

Detail

Features that are made by man, such as roads, are called man-made features.

Think About It

Form an Opinion

Review your research. What geographic features make California unique?

Write About It

In Your Opinion

What makes California geography different from other places in the United States?

_____

_____

_____

_____

_____

Write and Cite Evidence

List three reasons that support your opinion. Include page references.

_____

_____

_____

_____

_____

_____

_____

_____

_____

Talk About It

Explain

Take turns reading your writing with a classmate. Paraphrase your classmate's reasons and evidence and then discuss which reasons best support his or her opinion.

Geography

Connect to the

Consider

Think about the geographic features and natural resources you have learned about in this lesson. Why might the Central Valley region be a better place for agriculture than other regions? List your ideas to share with others.

_____

_____

_____

_____

_____

_____

Inquiry Project Notes

_____

_____

_____

_____

_____

How Did the First People Get to California?

Lesson Outcomes

What Am I Learning?

In this lesson, you're going to use your investigative skills to explore how the first people got to California and how they lived once they arrived.

Why Am I Learning It?

Reading and talking about how the first people came to California will help you learn more about human history in North America.

How Will I Know That I Learned It?

You will be able to explain how climate allowed people to **migrate** to California and how the area's natural features affected their lives.

Talk About It

COLLABORATE

Look closely at the picture. What are the natural features of this land? What are these people doing? How do you know?

HSS.4.1.3, HSS.4.1.4, HSS.4.2.1, HAS.CS.4, HAS.CS.5, HAS.HI.2

Long ago, people lived and hunted on Beringia.

Read Look at the title. What do you think this text will be about?

- **Circle** names of places.
- **Discuss** how California's geography played a role in the lives of early peoples.

My Notes

_____

_____

_____

_____

_____

_____

_____

_____

_____

_____

_____

_____

_____

_____

_____

_____

_____

Beringia

Where did the first Americans come from? How did they get to California? Scientists think the answer to these questions is Beringia.

Beringia was a land bridge that connected the continents of Asia and North America ten to twenty thousand years ago. During this time, large glaciers covered the land in North America. These large bodies of ice caused the sea level to drop 300 feet, exposing the dry land that formed the bridge.

The land bridge was not narrow like a manmade bridge would be today. Up to a thousand miles wide, Beringia was home to herds of large animals, such as the woolly mammoth and mastodon. Many other animals roamed the flat grasslands, including the brown bear, horse, and moose. Small groups of people from Asia migrated to Beringia. They followed the spread of plants and animals, hunting for food.

Over time, the glaciers melted, covering the land bridge with water. The melting glaciers also exposed the land in North America. The hunters migrated into North America, some traveling south to California. These first Californians made their homes throughout the land. Some lived near the coast of the Pacific Ocean. Others dwelled farther inland, in deserts, in valleys, or on mountains.

prehistoric stone tools

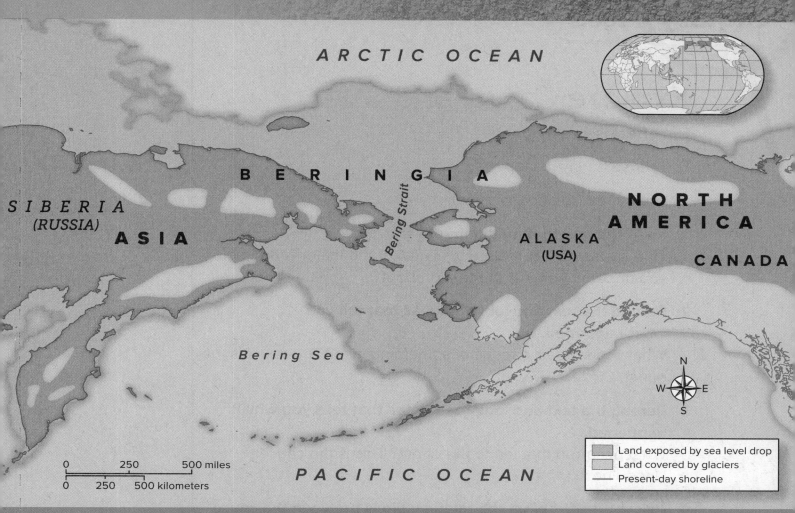

ARCTIC OCEAN

BERINGIA

SIBERIA
(RUSSIA)

ASIA

Bering Strait

NORTH
AMERICA

ALASKA
(USA)

CANADA

Bering Sea

| 0 | 250 | 500 miles |
| 0 | 250 | 500 kilometers |

PACIFIC OCEAN

N
W E
S

Land exposed by sea level drop
Land covered by glaciers
Present-day shoreline

Beringia

📍 **Map Skills** With a partner, read the labels on the map to determine the name of the body of water that covers Beringia and separates the North American and Asian continents.

2 Find Evidence

Reread Explain what caused early humans to leave Beringia.

Draw one line under causes. Draw two lines under effects.

In your explanation, be sure to describe the effects that glaciers in North America had on the migration of animals and people.

3 Make Connections

Talk Discuss with a partner why some areas of Beringia are different colors. Why is this information included on the map?

Then talk about other information that the map provides that is not in the text.

Explore Cause and Effect

The **effect** is what happened.

The **cause** is why it happened.

To find the cause and the effect:

1. **Read the text from beginning to end.**
   This gives you a complete overview of the material and helps you understand what the text is about.

2. **Reread the text and look for ideas that tell you what happened.**
   What occurred as a result of something else? The result is the effect. Circle it.

3. **Reread the text and look for a detail that tells you why it happened.**
   What occurred that led to the effect? This is the cause. Underline it.

4. **Ask yourself, "What the relationship is between the cause and the effect?"**
   How did one event lead to another?

 COLLABORATE Based on the text you read, work with your class to complete the chart below.

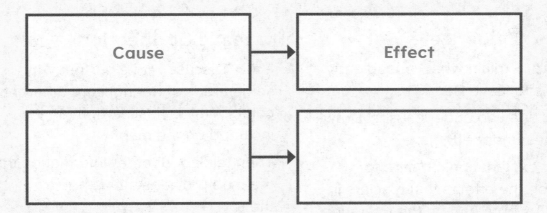

Cause		Effect
	→	
	→	

Investigate!

Read pages 26–35 in your Research Companion. Use your investigative skills to identify the causes and effects of the first peoples arriving in North America. This chart will help you organize your notes.

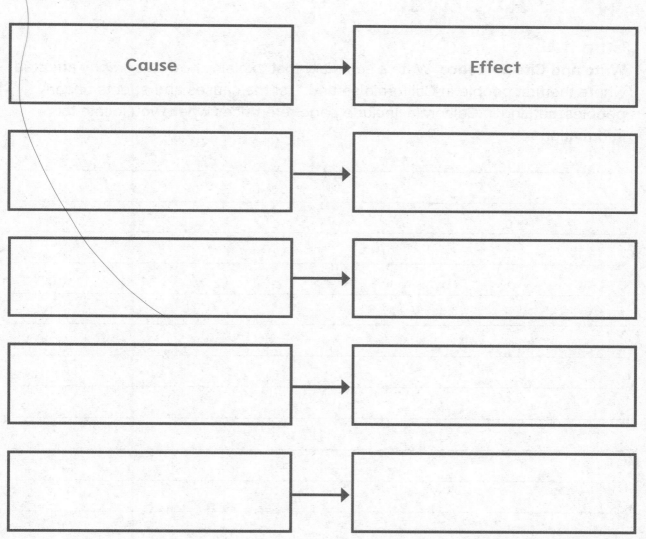

Cause → **Effect**

Think About It

Identify Effects

Review your research. How did geographic features affect how the first people got to California?

Write About It

Sum It Up

Write and Cite Evidence Write a summary that explains how geography affected where the first people in California settled. List the causes and effects of early peoples' settling in California. Include page references where you locate this information.

_____

_____

_____

_____

_____

_____

_____

_____

_____

_____

_____

_____

_____

_____

_____

Talk About It

Comprehend

With a classmate, discuss why traveling to and within California would have been challenging for early people. Use evidence from the text to support your ideas.

Geography

Connect to the

Pull It Together

Think about the lives of California's first people. How did geography affect where they settled and how they lived? List three cause-and-effect relationships below.

1. _____

_____

_____

2. _____

_____

_____

3. _____

_____

_____

Inquiry Project Notes

_____

_____

_____

_____

What Was Life Like for the Early Peoples of Central and Southern California?

Lesson Outcomes

What Am I Learning?

In this lesson, you're going to use your investigative skills to explore what life was like for California Indians living in Central and Southern California.

Why Am I Learning It?

Reading and talking about how people lived in California long ago will help you learn more about how geography impacts people.

How Will I Know That I Learned It?

You will be able to discuss what life was like in early California and identify similarities and differences among the many cultural groups who made California home.

Talk About It

Look closely at the picture. What is the person doing? What items or tools are they using?

HSS.4.1.3, HSS.4.2.1, EEI.PI, HAS.CS.4, HAS.CS.5, HAS.HI.2

Yokuts house with a bed made from tule reeds and animal skins

1 Inspect

Read Look at the title. What do you think the text will be about?

- **Circle** words you don't know.
- **Underline** details that answer the questions *What* and *How*.
- **Discuss** questions that the article does not have answers for.

My Notes

_____

_____

_____

_____

_____

_____

_____

_____

_____

_____

_____

_____

_____

_____

_____

Chumash Cave Paintings

High in the foothills of Santa Barbara county are ancient Chumash cave paintings. Historians believe that these cave paintings were a part of rituals conducted by shamans for religious purposes. The meanings behind the paintings are not clear. Often the Chumash themselves painted over older paintings. Some common themes and symbols can be seen, however. Crosses, spoked wheels, and zigzagged lines were often used.

The artists made paints. They used powders of different rocks and minerals to create paints of different colors. They ground up charcoal and manganese oxide for black. They used iron oxide called hematite for red. They used gypsum or diatomaceous earth for white. The powders were mixed with water, animal fat, egg, or another substance to make the paint. Brushes came from animal tails or sticks. Sometimes, artists used their fingers as well.

Weather and erosion have damaged many Chumash cave paintings. So has vandalism. As early as the first European settlers, people have been destroying or writing over the paintings they found in the caves. In 1906, one local put up an iron gate over one of the caves to help protect the paintings inside. Visitors still come from all over to see these records of Chumash life.

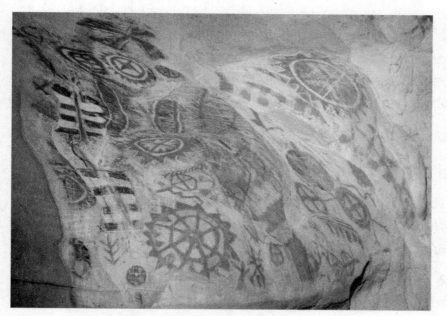

Cave paintings tell us about Chumash life.

PRIMARY SOURCE

In Their Words... Santa Ynez Band of Chumash Indians

"In the rolling hills of the coastline, our Chumash ancestors found caves to use for sacred religious ceremonies....Many of the caves still exist today, protected by the National Parks system, and illustrate the spiritual bond the Chumash hold with our environment."

—from "Chumash History" by the Santa Ynez Band of Chumash Indians

2 Find Evidence

Reread Why are the Chumash cave paintings important?

3 Make Connections

Talk Think about the Chumash cave paintings and what you know about the role of shamans in American Indian life. Discuss with a partner what purpose you think the cave paintings had and what they meant.

COLLABORATE

Explore Important Details

Details provide more information about the main idea of a text. Important details help readers to understand the topic. Important details can include examples, descriptions, or explanations.

To understand description:

1. **Read the text once all the way through.**

2. **Reread the text and look for signal words and phrases such as *for example* or *including*.** Why might some details be more important than others?

3. **Think about what the information helps you to understand.** Which details help you make sense of the text?

 COLLABORATE Based on the text you read, work with your class to complete the chart below.

Important Detail from Text	What It Explains	What It Helps Me Understand
Crosses, spoked wheels, and zigzagged lines were often used.		

Investigate!

Read pages 36-43 in your Research Companion. Use your investigative skills to identify details about the lives of early Central and Southern peoples in California.

Important Detail from Text	What It Explains	What It Helps Me Understand

Think About It

Sum Up

Review your research. How would you describe the lives of the early Central and Southern peoples in California?

Write About It

Write and Cite Evidence

Imagine that you lived in Central or Southern California as a Chumash or Yokuts in 1768. Write a journal entry that describes your daily life. Use important details as you write.

_____

_____

_____

_____

_____

_____

_____

_____

_____

_____

_____

_____

_____

_____

_____

_____

_____

Talk About It

Compare

Share your journal entry with a partner. Discuss how the lives of these particular California Indians were similar to and different from each other.

 History

Connect to the  EQ

Identify Relationships

How did the early peoples of Central and Southern California use what was available to live?

1. _____
_____
_____

2. _____
_____
_____

3. _____
_____
_____

EQ Inquiry Project Notes

_____
_____
_____
_____

How Did the Desert Peoples of California Use Their Environment?

Lesson Outcomes

What Am I Learning?

In this lesson, you're going to use your investigative skills to explore how the California Indians of the Great Basin and Colorado River culture areas adapted to their desert environment.

Why Am I Learning It?

Reading and talking about the desert peoples of the Great Basin and Colorado River will help you learn more about how people adapt to physical features and resources in their environment.

How Will I Know That I Learned It?

You will be able to explain ways that the Northern Paiute and Mohave Indians adapted to their desert environment, state an opinion about which geographic features or natural resources were most important to desert peoples, and support your opinion with evidence.

Talk About It

COLLABORATE

Read the primary source. What does it tell about how the Paiute used natural resources? What details of Paiute life do you think surprised the author of the article? How do you know?

HSS.4.1.3, HSS.4.2.1, HAS.CS.4, HAS.HI.2, HAS.HR.2

Tule rushes, or reed-like plants, covered wooden branches of this wikiup, much like the ones made by the Paiute.

PRIMARY SOURCE

As a people, the Paiute . . . [survive on] the fish of the lakes, jack rabbits and small game of the sage plains and mountains, and from pinon nuts and other seeds which they grind into flour for bread. Their ordinary dwelling is the wikiup or small rounded hut of tule rushes over a framework of poles, with the ground for a floor and the fire in the center and almost entirely open at the top. . .

[T]heir wikiups are almost bare of everything excepting a few wicker or grass baskets of their own weaving.

—From the newspaper *The Indian Advocate*, June 1901

Look at the photos. What information do they show?

- **Circle** words in the captions that you don't know.
- **Underline** a tool that could be used to carry seeds.
- **Circle** a tool with a hard surface for grinding.
- **Discuss** with a partner other uses for these tools.

My Notes

_____
_____
_____
_____
_____
_____
_____
_____
_____
_____
_____
_____
_____

Artifacts of Early Desert Peoples

Groups who lived in dry desert environments adapted to the desert's geographic features. They used its natural resources to survive. Their culture, traditions, and everyday tools and objects reflected life in a desert environment.

California indian water bottle, woven and covered in pitch

This painted Havasupai basket was used to carry supplies.

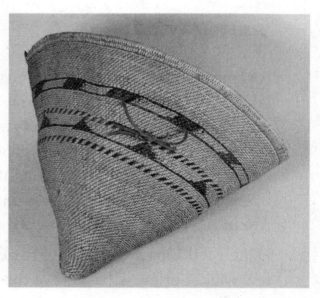

(t)Lebrecht Music and Arts Photo Library/Alamy; (b)NPS photo by Michael Quinn

Mohave Indians used a large stone, called a metate, and a small grinding stone, called a mano, to grind corn, wheat, and beans.

Coiled baskets like this one from the Washo tribe were used to carry things like seeds.

a pottery canteen from the Northern Paiute indians

(t)George Ostertag/Alamy; (c)Citizen of the Planet/Alamy; (b)B Christopher/Alamy

2 Find Evidence

Look Again What do the artifacts tell about how early desert people used their environment?

How did desert groups use natural resources to make everyday life easier? How can you tell that art was important, too?

3 Make Connections

Talk In a small group, discuss what the artifacts tell you about the everyday lives and activities of early desert peoples. Which artifacts on this page are similar to those shown in the photos on page 40?

COLLABORATE

Connect to Now What similar tools do we use today in everyday life?

Explore Main Idea and Details

Identifying key details in the text and visuals will help you better understand the big ideas about a topic. The **main idea** is the most important idea about a topic. **Details** give important information that supports the main idea.

1. **Read the text and look at the images.**
   This will help you understand the topic.

2. **Look for key details in the text and images.**
   Identify important details in the text and images. What do these details describe or explain? Why did the author include these images?

3. **Compare the key details in the text and images.**
   What idea do the important details in the text and images help to describe and show?

4. **Use key details to figure out the main idea.**
   Use key details to identify the main idea, or the most important point, about the topic.

 COLLABORATE Based on the text you read, and the photos you looked at, work with your class to complete the chart below.

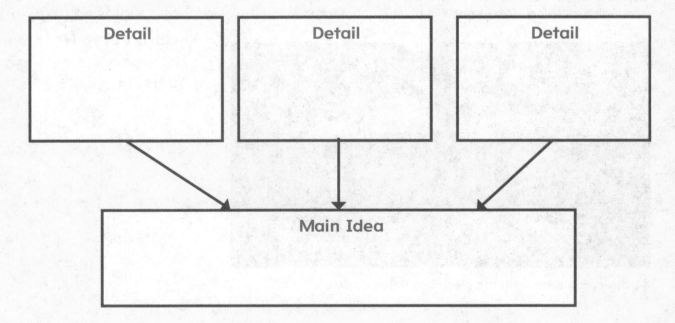

Detail	Detail	Detail

Main Idea

Investigate!

Read pages 44-53 in your Research Companion. Use your investigative skills to identify how desert people used the natural resources in their environment. Use the chart to organize information.

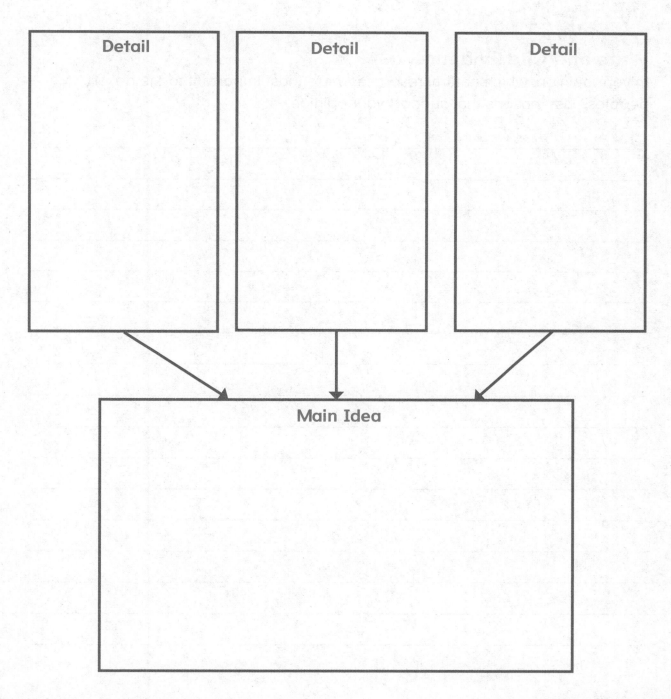

Detail

Detail

Detail

Main Idea

Think About It

Make Inferences

Review your research. Based on the information you have gathered, how do you think the Northern Paiute and Mohave Indians adapted to the natural resources of the desert?

Write About It

Write and Cite Evidence

In your opinion, which natural resources were most important to the desert peoples? List reasons that support your opinion.

_____

_____

_____

_____

_____

_____

_____

_____

_____

_____

_____

_____

_____

_____

_____

_____

Talk About It

COLLABORATE

Paraphrase

With a partner, take turns reading your opinions and supporting evidence. Paraphrase your partner's opinion and discuss why you agree or disagree with his or her opinion.

Geography

Connect to the

ESSENTIAL EQ QUESTION

Pull It Together

Think about the people and events that you read and talked about in this lesson. How did geography affect the desert peoples of California?

_____

_____

_____

_____

_____

_____

ESSENTIAL EQ QUESTION

Inquiry Project Notes

_____

_____

_____

_____

_____

_____

How Did the Resources of Northern California Impact the Early Peoples Living There?

Lesson Outcomes

What Am I Learning?

In this lesson, you're going to use your investigative skills to explore how the resources of Northern California affected the cultures of early peoples living there.

Why Am I Learning It?

Reading and talking about this information will help you understand the relationship between people and the natural environment.

How Will I Know That I Learned It?

You will be able to explain how early peoples adapted to the environment of Northern California and used its resources in everyday life.

Talk About It

Look closely at the picture. What natural resources do you see? How did they affect the peoples who lived in Northwest and Northeast California?

HSS.4.1.3, HSS.4.2.1, HAS.CS.4, HAS.CS.5, HAS.HI.2

A Hupa man looks for fish to spear.

Edward S. Curtis Collection, Library of Congress, LC-USZ62-113079

Read the title. What do you think this article is about? Why?

- **Circle** words that signal a cause.
- **Underline** words that signal an effect.

My Notes

_____
_____
_____
_____
_____
_____
_____
_____
_____
_____
_____
_____
_____
_____
_____
_____

The Living Canoes of the Yurok

The Yurok built large canoes from hollowed-out redwood logs. The canoes were an important part of their culture. The canoes made travel possible on the rivers and along the coast. The Yurok used these canoes to hunt for sea lions along the coast and to fish in the rivers and ocean. They also used the canoes to carry items to trade with other groups in the area. They could carry large loads because of the size of their canoes.

To the Yurok, the canoe was not just a means of transportation. They thought of it as a living being. So they made the parts of the canoe correspond to the organs of the human body. Each canoe had a nose, a heart, lungs, and kidneys. Because the canoes were made from the sacred redwood trees, the canoes were also seen as sacred. Therefore, canoes were also important in religious ceremonies.

A Yurok man paddles his canoe down a river.

Making a canoe was not easy. A canoe was dugout, or carved, from a giant redwood log. It took a long time and many people to complete. Anyone who owned a redwood canoe was thought to be very important.

The Yurok were different from other groups in California because they cared about wealth. They used a system of money based on shells. They made the shells into necklaces and decorated their clothing with them to display their wealth.

Look at the photo of the Yurok woman. What can you tell about her from looking at the photo?

2 Find Evidence

Reread What is an effect of the Yurok belief that the canoe was a living being?

Underline the details that help to show this effect.

Circle the effects of the Yurok belief in the collection of wealth.

3 Make Connections

Talk Discuss with a partner the reasons the Yurok made such large canoes.

COLLABORATE

Yurok woman wearing shell necklaces and clothing

The Protected Art Archive/Alamy

Explore Cause and Effect

The article "The Living Canoes of the Yurok" tells about the causes and effects of the Yurok building large canoes. It shows an **effect**—that is, what happened. It also shows a **cause**—why it happened. To find the cause and effect, follow these steps.

1. **Read the text once all the way through.**
   This will help you understand what the text is about.

2. **Reread the text, and look for a detail that tells you what happened.**
   This is the effect. Circle it.

3. **Reread the text again, and look for a detail that tells you why it happened.**
   This is the cause. Underline it.

4. **Explore the relationship between the cause and the effect.**
   Ask yourself, "How is the effect connected to the cause? How did one event lead to the other?"

 COLLABORATE Based on the text you read, work with your class to complete the diagram below.

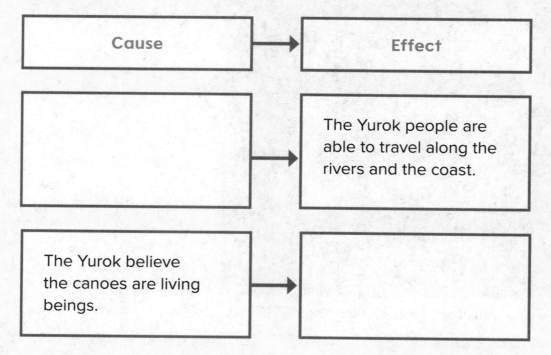

| Cause | → | Effect |

| | → | The Yurok people are able to travel along the rivers and the coast. |

| The Yurok believe the canoes are living beings. | → | |

Investigate!

Read pages 54–63 in your Research Companion. Use your investigative skills to identify text evidence that tells you about causes and effects. Focus on how the resources of Northern California affected the early peoples there. Use the chart to organize information.

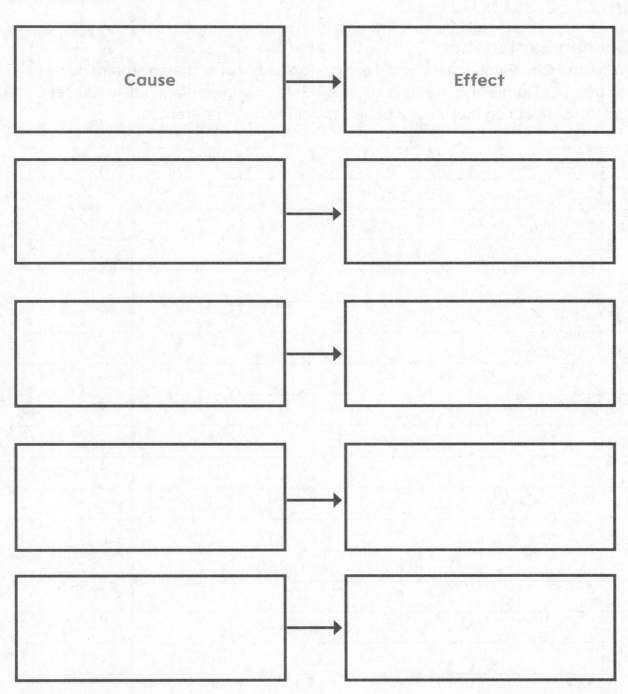

Cause		Effect
	→	
	→	
	→	
	→	
	→	

Think About It

Arrange the Facts

Review your research. Based on the information you have gathered, in what ways did natural resources impact the early peoples living in Northern California?

Write About It

Give an Explanation

Write and Cite Evidence How did early peoples adapt to the environment of Northern California and use its resources? Give examples of natural resources and their effects on these early peoples. Include page references.

_____
_____
_____
_____
_____
_____
_____
_____
_____
_____
_____
_____
_____
_____
_____
_____
_____

Talk About It

COLLABORATE

Paraphrase Ideas

Read your writing aloud to a partner. Take turns paraphrasing information and asking and answering questions about your key ideas.

Geography

Connect to the

Pull It Together

Think about what you've read and discussed in this lesson. How did geography influence the lives of early peoples living in Northern California?

_____

_____

_____

_____

_____

_____

_____

_____

Inquiry Project Notes

_____

_____

_____

_____

_____

_____

Inquiry Project Wrap Up

How Did Geography Affect the Settlement, Lives, and Interactions of California's Early Peoples?

Now's the time for you and your classmates to deliver an oral presentation. Here's what to do.

Use the statement you prepared to tell how geography affected California's early settlers.

☐ Present facts, details, and visual aids from your research as evidence in support of your statement.

☐ Answer questions from others about the evidence presented.

☐ Invite the class to discuss the question and the evidence in more depth.

Tips for Presenting

Remember these tips when you present to your class.

☐ Be sure to prepare and practice your presentation.

☐ Speak clearly at a confident, relaxed pace.

☐ Use visuals, such as maps, time lines, and pictures, when helpful.

Project Rubric

Use these questions to help evaluate your project.

	Yes	No
Did the facts and details show how geography influenced California's early peoples?		
Was the information organized in a sensible way and easy to understand?		
Did the visual aids help listeners grasp key ideas?		
Did the presentation include and demonstrate correct use of vocabulary from the chapter?		

Project Reflection

Think about the work you did to research and deliver your group's oral presentation. What did you find most satisfying? What would you like to improve for your next oral presentation?

_____

_____

_____

_____

_____

_____

Our Class Project to Save Salt Creek

CHARACTERS

Ms. Smith	Narrator	Raul
Kaitlyn	Jacob	Entire Class
Elizabeth		

Ms. Smith: This week, we've been discussing why it's important to protect our environment. Tomorrow we're going to break into teams, and each team is going to do a project about protecting the environment. Tonight, I want you to think about a project you and your teammates can work on together.

Kaitlyn: Oh, no. More homework!

Elizabeth: How are a few kids supposed to protect the environment?

Narrator: After school, Jacob and Raul walk home along Salt Creek after baseball practice.

Jacob: Are those old bottles and food wrappers near the creek?

Raul: Yeah, and check out that broken window over there.

Jacob: How did all this junk get here?

Raul:
People use the creek as a dumping ground. They just dump junk here, and bring more all the time. They have turned the creek into a garbage dump. What a shame! People used to enjoy the creek a lot more. My uncle told me that he used to go fishing here. He'd catch bass and pike and bring them home for his mom to cook.

Jacob: If there are any fish in that polluted water now, I wouldn't want to eat them. This place stinks.

Narrator: The boys soon arrive in front of Raul's house.

Jacob: Can we be on the same team in Ms. Smith's class?

Raul: Sure. Let's try to think of a great idea for the project!

Narrator: The next day, Ms. Smith organizes the class into teams. Raul, Jacob, Kaitlyn, and Elizabeth are on the same team.

Kaitlyn: Okay, has anybody thought of a good project yet?

Raul: Jacob and I talked about our ideas yesterday. I think we should clean up Salt Creek so people can use it for fishing again.

Jacob: Wow, that's a lot of work!

Kaitlyn and Elizabeth: Let's go look at the creek before we jump into this project.

Narrator: After school, Kaitlyn, Elizabeth, Jacob, and Raul visit the creek. Raul hands everyone large garbage bags. The kids fill the bags with bottles, tires, cans, food wrappers, paper, and other trash.

Fuse/Getty Images

Kaitlyn: We've only covered one small area. How are we going to be able to clean up the whole creek?

Elizabeth: I've got an idea. Why don't we ask Ms. Smith if the entire class can work on this project?

Raul: Now you're thinking!

Narrator: The next day the team tells the class about Salt Creek and Raul's idea to clean it up.

Ms. Smith: What do you think, class? Raise your hand if you'd like to do this project.

Narrator: Everyone's hand went up. Soon the entire class was working on clearing garbage around the creek. Every time they showed up, though, they would see new garbage. Back in class, the group talked about what to do about this problem.

Kaitlyn: Why do some people treat the creek like a garbage dump? The people who litter there should be punished.

Entire Class: We should put up a sign telling people not to dump garbage here.

Ms. Smith: These are both good ideas. Let's write to the city council and see if they can do anything to support our project.

Narrator: Soon a sign was posted near the creek. It said, "NO DUMPING AT THE CREEK. MINIMUM FINE $250." But there was still more to do to protect the creek.

Ms. Smith: Class, you've done a great job so far. But we still need to do something about the garbage in the creek that we can't pick up.

Entire Class: What's the kind of garbage that we can't pick up?

Ms. Smith: When people wash their cars or change the oil in their car, sometimes the dirty water or oil goes down the drain in the street. The rain then carries that polluted water into Salt Creek.

Entire Class: How are we supposed to stop people from getting dirty water in the street drains?

Kaitlyn: Where my cousin lives, they have signs on the drains to remind people that whatever goes down them will end up in the river.

Narrator: The class painted signs on storm drains that led to the creek. "Don't Dump Waste. Drains to Stream."

Ms. Smith: Class, I have an announcement to make. You did an amazing job on this project. What a great accomplishment!

Write About It

Write your own Reader's Theater play about an environmental project.

Chapter 2

A Spanish Colony in California

ESSENTIAL **EQ** QUESTION

What Changes Did Spanish Explorers Bring to California?

In this chapter, you'll explore how and why Spanish explorers came to California. You'll also read about how the Spanish influenced society, including the California Indians' way of life.

Talk About It

COLLABORATE

Discuss with a partner questions you have about the Spanish coming to California. As you research the people, events, and ideas from these early days of colonization, look for answers to your questions. Let's get started!

My Research Questions

1. _____

   _____

2. _____

   _____

3. _____

   _____

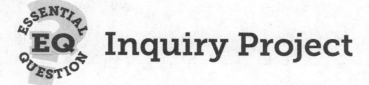 Inquiry Project

Walking in the Shoes of the Spanish in California

In this project, you'll work with a team to write and perform a play. First, you'll identify the important ideas in this chapter. You might describe the explorers leaving Spain, arriving in California, or the start of the mission system. Determine which viewpoints you will present. Create scenery and collect props. Perform your play for the group or videotape the performance. Allow time for audience feedback and questions.

Here's your project checklist.

☐ **Identify** the major idea from the chapter that your play will tell about.

☐ **Outline** the story and begin to write.

☐ **Determine** and assign roles.

☐ **Demonstrate** a point of view through dialogue.

☐ **Create** simple scenery, collect props, and gather costumes.

☐ **Perform** for an audience or **videotape** your performance.

☐ **Seek** feedback and answer questions.

Explore Words

Complete this chapter's Word Rater.
Write notes as you learn more about each word.

colony
- ☐ Know It!
- ☐ Heard It!
- ☐ Don't Know It!

My Notes
_____
_____
_____

convert
- ☐ Know It!
- ☐ Heard It!
- ☐ Don't Know It!

My Notes
_____
_____
_____

empire
- ☐ Know It!
- ☐ Heard It!
- ☐ Don't Know It!

My Notes
_____
_____
_____

inhabitants
- ☐ Know It!
- ☐ Heard It!
- ☐ Don't Know It!

My Notes
_____
_____
_____

mission
- ☐ Know It!
- ☐ Heard It!
- ☐ Don't Know It!

My Notes
_____
_____
_____

presidios

☐ Know It!
☐ Heard It!
☐ Don't Know It!

My Notes

_____
_____
_____

pueblos

☐ Know It!
☐ Heard It!
☐ Don't Know It!

My Notes

_____
_____
_____

rebel

☐ Know It!
☐ Heard It!
☐ Don't Know It!

My Notes

_____
_____
_____

revolt

☐ Know It!
☐ Heard It!
☐ Don't Know It!

My Notes

_____
_____
_____

trapper

☐ Know It!
☐ Heard It!
☐ Don't Know It!

My Notes

_____
_____
_____

Why Did Spanish Explorers Come to California?

Lesson Outcomes

What Am I Learning?
In this lesson, you're going to use your investigative skills to explore why Spanish explorers came to California.

Why Am I Learning It?
Reading and talking about why Spanish explorers came to California will help you understand their impact on this region of North America. It will also help you understand the region's later development into the state of California.

How Will I Know that I Learned It?
You will be able to identify the chronology of Spanish exploration of this region. You will be able to state an opinion about how Spanish explorers affected the development of the territory. You will be able to support your opinion with evidence.

Talk About It

COLLABORATE

Look closely at the maps. What difference do you see between the ancient map and the modern one? What could explain the difference?

HSS.4.2.2, HSS.4.2.3, HAS.CS.1

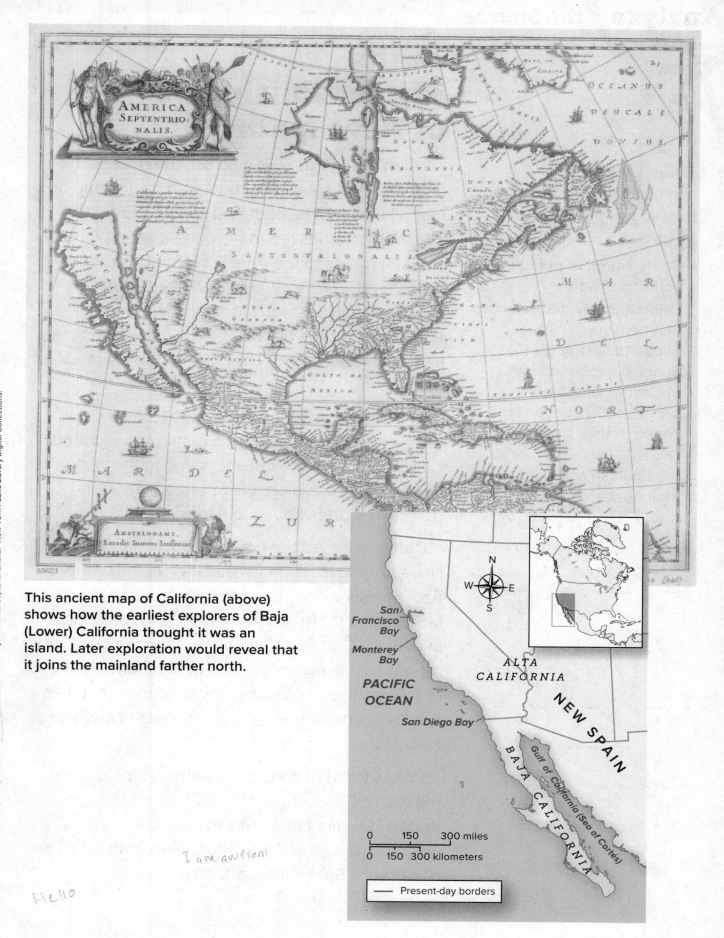

This ancient map of California (above) shows how the earliest explorers of Baja (Lower) California thought it was an island. Later exploration would reveal that it joins the mainland farther north.

Analyze the Source

1 Inspect

Read Look at the title and headings. What do they suggest the text will be about?

- **Circle** words or phrases you don't know.
- **Underline** key details that help you understand why the Spanish explorers came to California and how previous discoveries changed their goals.
- **Discuss** with a partner if the Spanish achieved their goals.

My Notes

_____
_____
_____
_____
_____
_____
_____
_____

The Establishment of New Spain

When Columbus sailed across the Atlantic, he hoped to find a new sea route to Asia. Instead he found lands that he had not expected to find. These discoveries led to new goals for exploration. The sea routes to the Americas that Columbus discovered were soon used by other Spanish explorers called *conquistadors*. These were Spanish soldiers who took by force the lands that had been discovered. They claimed these lands for Spain.

One of these *conquistadors* was Hernán Cortés. Cortés knew about the land Columbus had found. Cortés left Spain in 1504 and sailed to the Western Hemisphere to explore the territory himself. In particular, Cortés hoped to find gold.

Cortés reached the city of Tenochtitlán in November 1519. This city was the capital of the Aztec **empire**. The ruler of the Aztec was Montezuma II. He greeted Cortés with presents. Eventually Cortés defeated the Aztec and reached his goal of taking possession of their land. The land of the Aztec and other nearby territories that the Spanish captured became the Spanish **colony** of New Spain.

Cortés then led another expedition, sailing along the Pacific Coast of what is now Mexico. His ship landed in an area that came to be known as Baja California, or Lower California. The Spanish called this part of New Spain "the Californias."

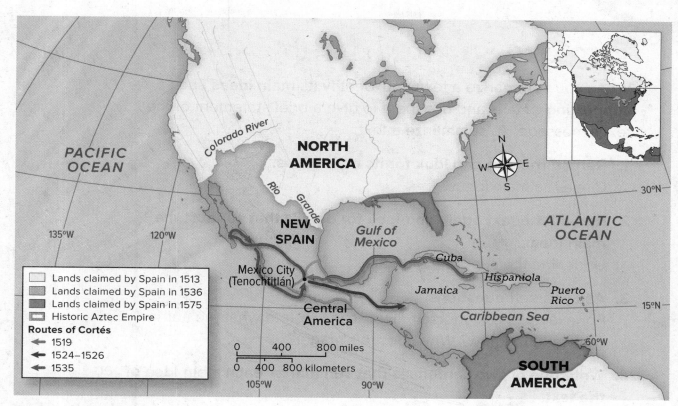

Routes of Cortés

Map Legend:
- Lands claimed by Spain in 1513
- Lands claimed by Spain in 1536
- Lands claimed by Spain in 1575
- Historic Aztec Empire

Routes of Cortés
- 1519
- 1524–1526
- 1535

Map Labels: PACIFIC OCEAN, NORTH AMERICA, Colorado River, Rio Grande, NEW SPAIN, Gulf of Mexico, Mexico City (Tenochtitlán), Central America, Cuba, Jamaica, Hispaniola, Puerto Rico, Caribbean Sea, ATLANTIC OCEAN, SOUTH AMERICA

Coordinates: 135°W, 120°W, 105°W, 90°W, 60°W, 30°N, 15°N

Scale: 0 400 800 miles / 0 400 800 kilometers

2 Find Evidence

Reread How does the text help you understand why Spanish explorers came to the New World?

Based on the meaning of *conquistadors*, did you expect what happened to the Aztecs? Explain your reasoning.

3 Make Connections

Talk Discuss with a partner how the goals of the Spanish explorers changed as they learned more from their explorations.

Talk about how the events you have read about affected the region the Spanish explorers found.

Explore Summarizing

When you **summarize** a text, you identify its **main ideas** and **supporting details** and use them to give a brief statement of the text's message. To summarize a text:

1. **Reread the text and look for its main ideas.**
   Circle the main ideas.

2. **Reread the text again and look for details that support the main ideas.**
   Underline the supporting details.

3. **Ask yourself questions.**
   For example, ask yourself, "How can I restate what the author wants me to know? Why does this matter?"

4. **Write one or two sentences that summarize each main idea of the text.**

COLLABORATE Based on the text you read, work with your class to complete the chart below.

Main Idea The Establishment of New Spain

_____

_____

Detail 1 _____

_____

Detail 2 _____

_____

↓

Summary _____

_____

_____

_____

Investigate!

Read pages 74–81 in your Research Companion. Use your investigative skills to summarize the text. Use this chart to organize your information.

Main Idea 1	Main Idea 2	Main Idea 3
_____	_____	_____
_____	_____	_____
Detail 1 _____	Detail 1 _____	Detail 1 _____
_____	_____	_____
Detail 2 _____	Detail 2 _____	Detail 2 _____
_____	_____	_____

Summary _____

_____

_____

_____

Think About It

Make Inferences

Review your research. Based on the information you have gathered, what do you think it was like to sail on an expedition to explore California? What sights did the explorers see? What adventures did they have? What challenges did they face?

Write About It

Organize an Expedition

Write and Cite Evidence Using text evidence, create an advertising brochure to interest people in joining Cabrillo's Spanish expedition to California. The brochure should include the following information:

- the goals of the trip
- a map of the route the explorers will take
- the supplies they will need to take
- the American Indians they may meet
- the landscape and climate they will encounter
- the challenges they may face
- the personality traits they will need to succeed

Include at least one picture and one map in the brochure.

Talk About It

Be Persuasive

Present your brochure to a partner as though you are trying to convince him or her to take the voyage. Then switch roles and listen to your partner's presentation. Share feedback about each other's work.

 History

Connect to the

Pull It Together

Think about the events that you read and talked about in this lesson. Why did the European explorers come to California? How did what they found change their plans? What changes did they themselves bring to California?

_____

_____

_____

_____

_____

_____

_____

Inquiry Project Notes

_____

_____

_____

What Was Spain's Plan to Colonize California?

Lesson Outcomes

What Am I Learning?

In this lesson, you're going to use your investigative skills to explore Spain's plan to colonize California.

Why Am I Learning It?

Reading and talking about the plan for colonizing California will help you understand Spain's reason for interest in California and the relationships among missionaries, soldiers, and California Indians.

How Will I Know That I Learned It?

You will be able to explain what the plan was to colonize California and cite evidence about whether or not it was a well-designed plan.

Talk About It

Look closely at the picture. What do you notice about the location of the buildings? Why do you think the colonists chose this spot as a place to build?

HSS.4.2.2, HSS.4.2.3, HAS.CS.5

72 Lesson 2 What Was Spain's Plan to Colonize California?

Colonists built the San Diego church on a hill close to water.

Analyze the Source

1 Inspect

Read Look at the title. What do you think this text will be about?

- **Highlight** words that explain *"Sacred Expedition"* and *mission*.
- **Circle** similarities between the San Diego and La Asunción sites.
- **Underline** words in Crespí's diary entry that tell us more about his impressions of the California Indians.

My Notes

_____

_____

_____

_____

_____

_____

_____

_____

_____

Plans for Alta California

The "Sacred Expedition" was the plan of religious importance that Spain had for settling California. The plan was to travel north from Mexico to build missions in Alta, or Upper, California. A **mission** was a religious community where Spanish priests taught California Indians the Roman Catholic faith. The mission church was the center of the community.

During the "Sacred Expedition," a few travelers kept diaries. These diaries help us understand the ideas and plans the colonists had for California.

Most diary entries identify the date or number of days in a place. Some passages describe the geography of the area, including the desert, mountains, plants, animals, and access to water. Others describe the Native people that the colonists met along the way. The following diary entry shows the perspective of Father Juan Crespí as he explored California.

In his diary entry dated August 14, Father Crespí is in La Asunción. He describes the geography of La Asunción as a piece of land that sits above the water. He describes the California Indians as "active" people who were good at making things using wooden or stone tools. He thinks it would be a good place for a mission.

McGraw-Hill Education, TEXT: Bolton, Herbert Eugene. *Fray Juan Crespi: Missionary Explorer on the Pacific Coast 1769-1774.* Berkeley: University of California Press, 1927.

PRIMARY SOURCE

In Their Words... Father Juan Crespí

"According to the number of people whom we saw and who came down from the camp, there were not less than four hundred souls.

They are of good figure and disposition, active, industrious, and inventive. They have surprising skill and ability in the construction of their canoes...

...The soldiers traded beads with them in exchange for baskets, pebbles, and wooden plates which would not be more graceful if they were turned with a wheel. They gave us a lot of fish, expecially very savory bonito. Judging by the great abundance of it and the ease with which it was caught, this must be the season for it."

—translated from Father Juan Crespí's diary
Monday, August 14

Father Juan Crespí was a Spanish missionary during the "Sacred Expedition."

2 Find Evidence

Reread Find details that illustrate how Father Crespí sees his role from a religious viewpoint.

Describe Crespí's viewpoint about the California Indians.

3 Make Connections

Draw Draw an image that shows the type of place that the colonists wanted to find for their missions. Turn back to page 74. What type of geographical features did they want? Who would live there?

Explore Main Idea and Details

Finding the main idea and details is a strategy to help you explain the most important parts of a text.

The **topic** is what the reading is about.

The **main idea** is an important point that the author makes about the topic.

The **details** give supporting information and tell more about the main idea.

To find the main idea:

1. **Look at the title and headings, and make a prediction about the topic.**
   Ask yourself "What am I going to read about?"

2. **Read the text once all the way through.**
   Get a sense of what the text is telling you about the topic.

3. **Reread the text.**
   Circle important details, words, information, and ideas that are repeated or emphasized.

4. **Look at your list of details or common words for patterns.**
   Identify how your details are related. What important point or big idea do the details help to explain? This is the main idea.

COLLABORATE Based on the text you read, work with your class to complete the chart below.

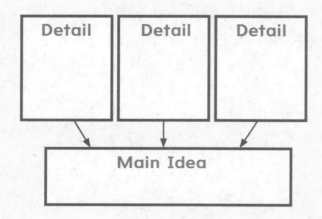

Investigate!

Read pages 82–89 in your Research Companion. Use your investigative skills to identify the main idea and the important details of Spain's plan to colonize California. This chart will help you organize your notes.

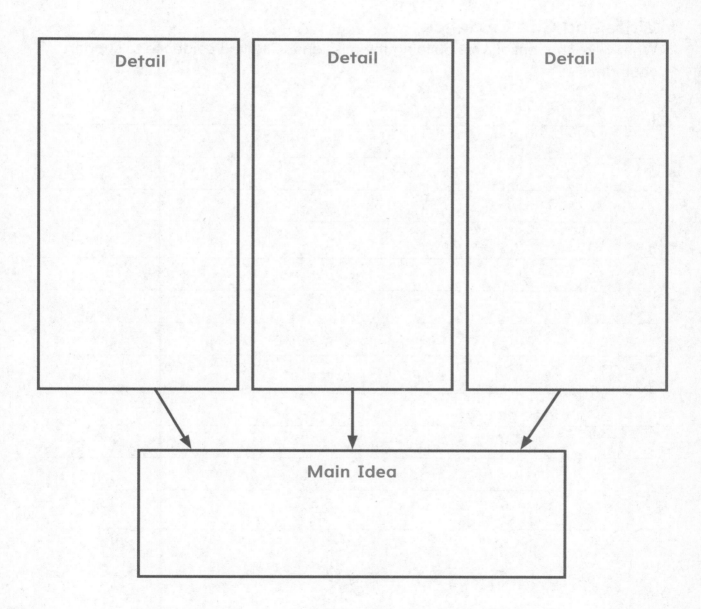

Detail

Detail

Detail

Main Idea

Think About It

Sum Up
Review your research. Based on the information you have gathered, what challenges did Spain face as they began colonizing California?

Write About It

Write and Cite Evidence
What were the reasons for building the missions? Cite text evidence to support your ideas.

1. _____

_____

_____

_____

2. _____

_____

_____

_____

3. _____

_____

_____

_____

_____

Talk About It

Debate

Talk with a partner about Spain's plan to colonize California. Explain why you agree or disagree with the reasons for the missions.

 History

Connect to the

Pull It Together

How did Spain's plan to colonize California have an impact on the lives of the Indians?

_____

_____

_____

_____

_____

_____

_____

_____

Inquiry Project Notes

_____

_____

_____

_____

_____

What Was Life Like in the Missions?

Lesson Outcomes

What Am I Learning?
In this lesson, you're going to use your investigative skills to understand how California Indians were changed by life in the missions.

Why Am I Learning It?
Reading and talking about what life was like for California Indians in the missions will help you learn more about how the Spanish changed the way of life for many of the California Indians.

How Will I Know That I Learned It?
You will be able to explain how the mission system expanded Catholicism to North America and impacted the California Indians' way of life.

Talk About It

Look at the picture Where are these people? What is the relationship between the missionaries (men on horses) and the California Indians? How do you know?

HSS.4.2.3, HSS.4.2.4, HSS.4.2.5, HSS.4.2.6

Many California Indians lived at the missions with the Spanish missionaries. This is Carmel Mission.

Mission Way of Life

At the missions, the California Indians followed a structured pattern of daily prayer and endured forced labor. In most missions, California Indians were not allowed to have their own religious ceremonies. Most did not enjoy living in missions, but Spanish soldiers forced them to stay.

Instead of hunting and gathering, the California Indians in the missions grew food and tended livestock. In many missions, the California Indians were required to make their own clothing and to dress like the missionaries. The California Indian way of life and dress were often replaced by the mission ways.

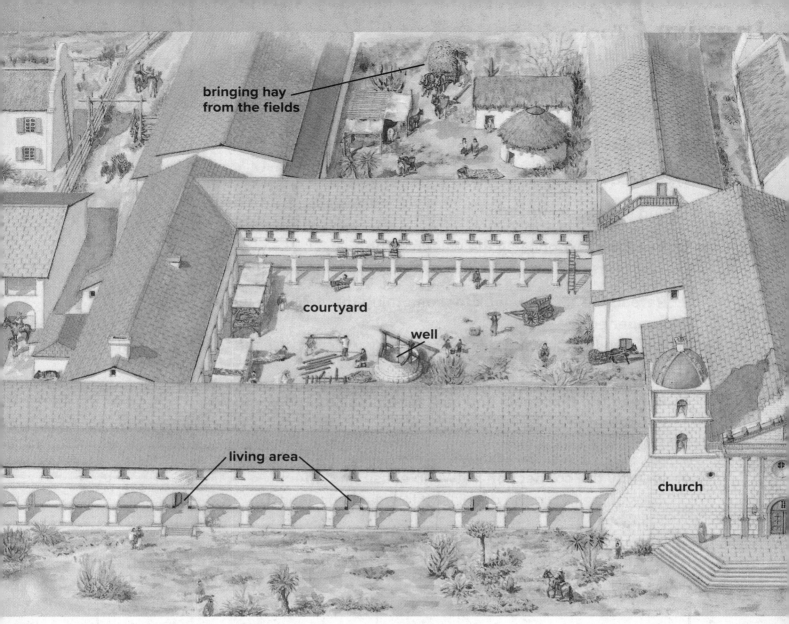

bringing hay from the fields

courtyard

well

living area

church

This overhead view shows different parts of a California mission.

2 Find Evidence

Reread How did mission life compare to life in California Indian villages?

What kind of skills did California Indians have before the missions? What kind of skills do you think they learned after living in the missions?

3 Make Connections

Write What kind of changes did the missions bring for the California Indians? What effect did the missions have on the their culture? Using the illustration and text, write two sentences to answer these questions.

Explore Cause and Effect

The **effect** is what happened.

The **cause** is why it happened.

To find the cause and effect:

1. **Read the text once all the way through.**
   This gives you a complete overview of the material.

2. **Reread the text and look for something that tells you what happened.**
   This can be an event or the result of some action. It is the effect. Circle it.

3. **Reread the text again and look for a detail that tells you why it happened.**
   This is the cause. Underline it.

4. **Identify the connection between cause and effect.**
   Ask yourself, "Did the detail lead to what happened?"

 COLLABORATE Based on the text you read, work with your class to complete the chart below.

Cause	Effect
Missions required the California Indians to work, pray, and dress like the Spanish.	

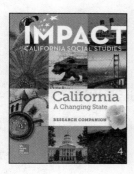

Investigate!

Read pages 90–99 in your Research Companion. Use your investigative skills to identify the purpose of the missions, why the California Indians lived in missions, and how the missions affected their lives. This chart will help you organize your notes.

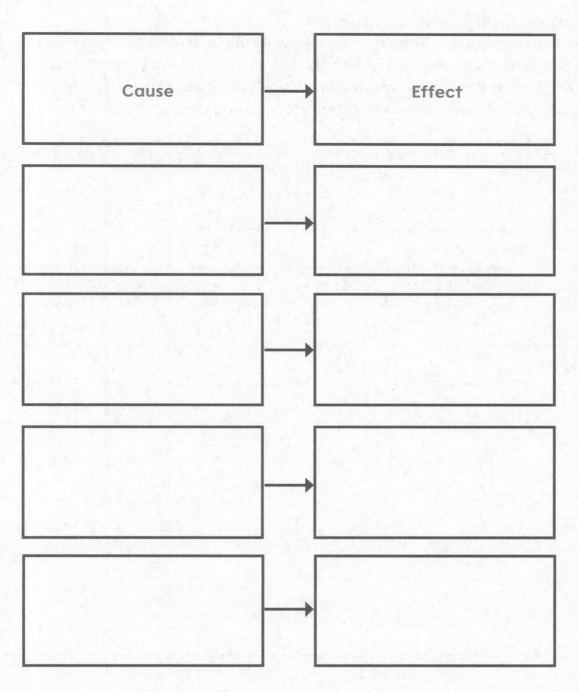

Cause ⟶ Effect

Think About It

Sum Up
Review your research. How did Spanish and California Indian cultures interact?

Write About It

Create a Diary or Journal Entry
Write a diary or journal entry for a day or week in the life of a Spanish missionary or a California Indian living in a mission. Begin by describing yourself. Share your emotions. How does it feel to live in a mission? What do you see around you? What do you do? How are you treated? How do you view life here?

_____

_____

_____

_____

_____

_____

_____

_____

_____

_____

_____

_____

Talk About It

COLLABORATE

Support Your Viewpoint

Read your journal entry aloud to a partner. Take turns discussing how the viewpoints are supported by evidence.

History

Connect to the

ESSENTIAL EQ QUESTION

Pull It Together

What effect did the missions have on the lives of California Indians?

_____

_____

_____

_____

_____

_____

_____

_____

ESSENTIAL EQ QUESTION

Inquiry Project Notes

_____

_____

_____

_____

_____

_____

How Did Spanish Settlers Transform the Region?

Lesson Outcomes

What Am I Learning?

In this lesson, you're going to use your investigative skills to explore how the arrival of Spanish settlers changed California.

Why Am I Learning It?

Reading and talking about these changes will help you understand the settlement of California by the Spanish.

How Will I Know That I Learned It?

You will be able to explain how California changed after the arrival of the Spanish.

Talk About It

Look closely at the picture. How would you describe this place? Why do you think it has a wall around it?

HSS.4.2.4, HSS.4.2.5, HSS.4.2.6, HAS.CS.4, HAS.CS.5

88 Lesson 4 How Did Spanish Settlers Transform the Region?

diagram of a **presidio** located in California

Soldiers' home

Commander's house

Private gardens

Guardhouse

Outer defense wall

Images From the Past

1 Inspect

Look Focus on the people in the images and read the captions and text. How are the two groups of people similar? How are they different?

Analyze details that tell you:

- what California was like before the Spanish arrived
- what California was like after the Spanish arrived

Circle details in the images, captions, and text that help you understand how the Spanish transformed California.

My Notes

_____

_____

_____

_____

_____

PRIMARY SOURCE

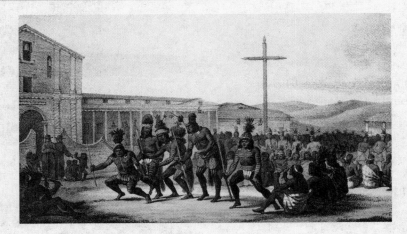

In this Illustration by Louis Choris, California Indians of Mission San Francisco de Asís are shown in traditional dress.

Before the Spanish came to settle California, the California Indians had their own culture and traditions. They had their own religion—believing in a spirit world with a shaman as the religious leader.

antique print of mission Indians of Southern California, 1890

2 Find Evidence

Look Again How do the images help you understand the differences in California before and after the arrival of the Spanish?

Pay attention to details. Which clues seem most important?

3 Make Connections

Talk Discuss with a partner how the two images are different.

Share ideas about how the images show the influence of Spanish settlers in California.

For the California Indians, life during the mission period was very different from before. While living in the missions, the California Indians received training in the Christian faith. The missionaries expected them to give up their culture and religious beliefs.

Explore Compare and Contrast

Authors often write to **compare** (to show how things are the same or similar) or to **contrast** (to show how things are different). Sometimes authors use signal words like *same* or *both* when they compare. Sometimes they use signal words like *than*, *but*, or *however* when they contrast. Sometimes they don't use signal words at all. When that happens, you still can compare and contrast on your own.

To compare and contrast:

1. **Look at the images and read the captions and text once, all the way through.**
   This will help you understand what the images are about.

2. **Look again at the images and reread the captions and text.**
   Make sure you understand the most important details.

3. **Look for differences in a topic.**
   For example, how did religious worship of the California Indians change after the Spanish came to the area?

 Based on the images you looked at and captions and text you read, compare and contrast California before and after the arrival of the Spanish. Work with your class to complete the diagram below.

	Before Mission Period	During Mission Period
Communities		
Land Use		
Culture		
People		

Investigate!

Read pages 100–107 in your Research Companion. Use your investigative skills to compare and contrast details about what California was like before and after the arrival of the Spanish. Use this chart to organize your information.

	Before Mission Period	During Mission Period
Communities		
Land Use		
Culture		
People		

Report / Your Findings

Think About It

Make Inferences
Review your research. Based on the information you have gathered, in what ways did the arrival of the Spanish affect the region?

Write About It

Compare and Contrast
Draw two pictures on a separate sheet of paper. Show what life was like in California before and after the Spanish arrived.

Write and Cite Evidence
Write a paragraph to explain your two pictures.

_____

_____

_____

_____

_____

_____

_____

_____

_____

_____

Talk About It

Explain

Exchange drawings and read aloud your paragraph to a partner. Take turns discussing your responses. How are the details in your drawings and paragraphs similar and different?

History
Connect to the

Pull It Together

Think about how the arrival of the Spanish changed the region's culture, economy, and environment. How did these changes shape the history of California?

_____

_____

_____

_____

_____

_____

_____

_____

_____

Inquiry Project Notes

_____

_____

_____

Inquiry Project Wrap Up

Walking in the Shoes of the Spanish in California

Now's the time for you and your classmates to share your plays. Here's what to do.

Use your performance to help your audience understand an important idea about the Spanish explorers coming to California.

☐ Demonstrate a point of view about the arrival of the Spanish explorers through dialogue and actions.

☐ Use evidence from your research to defend the points of view you present.

☐ Allow time for audience feedback and questions.

Tips for Presenting a Play

Remember these tips when you present to your class.

☐ Memorize your lines and rehearse.

☐ Use gestures, expression, and an effective rate of speaking.

☐ Incorporate sound effects, scenery, costumes, and props into your performance.

Project Rubric

Use these questions to help evaluate your project.

	Yes	No
Did our play tell about the Spanish explorers' arrival to California?		
Did our play reveal a point of view through dialogue?		
Did our play include details that were based on evidence from our research?		
Did our play use words from the chapter vocabulary?		
Did our performance accurately reflect the key ideas we wanted to tell?		

Project Reflection

Think about the group project you did for this chapter. Describe your strongest contribution to the play. Describe what you could have done better. If you performed the play again, what would you change?

_____

_____

_____

_____

_____

_____

Chapter 3

Mexican California

ESSENTIAL EQ QUESTION

How Did California Change During the Period of Mexican Rule?

In this chapter, you'll discover how Mexico's War for Independence changed life in California. You'll find out how mission lands, which had once belonged to California Indians, became ranchos.

Talk About It

COLLABORATE

Discuss with a partner questions you have about California under Mexican rule. As you research how life in California changed, look for answers to your questions. Let's get started!

My Research Questions

1. _____

_____

2. _____

_____

3. _____

_____

Inquiry Project

Write with a Point of View

In this project, you'll write a story about how California changed during the period of Mexican rule.

Here's your project checklist.

☐ **Discuss** historical figures you've read about who lived during this time. Identify the figure who most interests you.

☐ **Recall** facts, quotes, and other details about this figure. Consider his or her point of view. What might he or she have thought and felt about the events of that period?

☐ **Plan** your story. Decide on the setting and the conflict or problem. Outline the plot, including the resolution of the conflict or problem.

☐ **Invite** your classmates to suggest edits and offer other feedback on your first draft.

☐ **Enhance** your story with technology. For example, present your story with slide presentation software.

☐ **Present** your story. Invite others to compare your historical figure's point of view with theirs.

Explore Words

Complete this chapter's Word Rater.
Write notes as you learn more about each word.

Californio
My Notes

☐ Know It!
☐ Heard It!
☐ Don't Know It!

immigrant
My Notes

☐ Know It!
☐ Heard It!
☐ Don't Know It!

land grant
My Notes

☐ Know It!
☐ Heard It!
☐ Don't Know It!

mestizo
My Notes

☐ Know It!
☐ Heard It!
☐ Don't Know It!

opportunity
My Notes

☐ Know It!
☐ Heard It!
☐ Don't Know It!

pioneer

My Notes

☐ Know It!

☐ Heard It!

☐ Don't Know It!

_____

_____

_____

revert

My Notes

☐ Know It!

☐ Heard It!

☐ Don't Know It!

_____

_____

_____

risk

My Notes

☐ Know It!

☐ Heard It!

☐ Don't Know It!

_____

_____

_____

trailblazer

My Notes

☐ Know It!

☐ Heard It!

☐ Don't Know It!

_____

_____

_____

vaquero

My Notes

☐ Know It!

☐ Heard It!

☐ Don't Know It!

_____

_____

_____

Why Did the California Indians Rebel?

Lesson Outcomes

What Am I Learning?
In this lesson, you're going to use your investigative skills to explore why California Indians rebelled against the missions.

Why Am I Learning It?
Reading and talking about the rebellions of the California Indians will help you understand that many California Indians were dissatisfied with life at the missions.

How Will I Know That I Learned It?
You will be able to describe different points of view, explain why California Indians rebelled, and support your explanation with evidence.

Talk About It

Inspect Look closely at the painting. What does the painting show about life in a mission? What do the details help you determine about the people and what they are doing?

HSS.4.2.5: HAS.HR.1, HAS.HR.2, HAS.HR.3

McGraw-Hill Education

Missionaries, Spanish soldiers, and California Indians lived and worked in missions.

Analyze the Source

1 Inspect

Read Look at the title. What does it tell you about the topic of the text?

- **Circle** important facts and details that answer the questions *Who, What, Where, When,* or *Why.*
- **Underline** words and phrases that describe or relate to a rebellion.
- **Discuss** the meaning of *rebellion,* and identify a synonym in the text.

My Notes

_____
_____
_____
_____
_____
_____
_____
_____
_____
_____
_____
_____
_____

Revolt Against Mission San Diego

Early in the morning in November 1775, a group of California Indians led a rebellion against Mission San Diego. Many California Indians did not want the missions on their homelands. Many were angry about how the Spanish were treating their people and changing their ways of life. Members of at least fifteen Indian villages joined in the attack. They entered the mission in the middle of the night. Some people living at the mission were killed. Others were injured. The rebels set fire to the buildings. By morning, Mission San Diego was completely destroyed.

The leaders of the revolt were believed to be two California Indian brothers known as Francisco and Carlos. The brothers had run away from Mission San Diego a month earlier. After their escape, they began speaking out against Mission San Diego. They persuaded other angry California Indians to join in their revolt.

Despite the destruction of the mission, the missionaries remained. Spanish soldiers captured Francisco, Carlos, and others who took part in the revolt. The missionaries asked the Spanish authorities to spare their lives. Francisco and Carlos returned to the mission and helped to rebuild it.

Father Junípero Serra was the founder of Mission San Diego.

2 Find Evidence

Reread Was the attack on the mission unorganized or carefully planned by the California Indians? What details in the article support your answer?

Do you think the rebellion was a success? What details explain the effects of the rebellion on the mission and the leaders of the revolt?

3 Make Connections

Talk Discuss the reasons Francisco or Carlos may have given to their friends or family for taking part in the rebellion.

COLLABORATE

Explore Point of View

Identifying a point of view, or position, can help you understand a perspective on people and events in history.

1. **Read the text all the way through.**
   This will help you understand what the text is about.

2. **Find details that tell about a position that is presented.**
   Which person or group is represented? How do you know?

3. **Notice facts and details.**
   What facts and details are included about the topic?

4. **Identify details that tell how the person or group feels.**
   Look for words that provide clues to a person's or a group's feelings about the missions or the reasons and evidence the person or group uses to support a view about the missions.

COLLABORATE Based on the text you read, work with your class to complete the chart below.

Person or Group	How did they feel about the missions?	How do you know? What details show their point of view?
Francisco and Carlos		

Investigate!

Read pages 118–127 in your Research Companion. Use your investigative skills to identify different points of view about the missions. This chart will help you organize your notes.

Person or Group	How do they feel about the missions?	How do you know? What details show their point of view?
Missionaries	The missionaries feel like they are doing god's work and are helping the indians.	For example, they thought that the Catholic religion was the best religion you could follow, so they thought they were
Soldiers	Some soldiers enjoyed the California Missions. Other soldiers did not like their duties in the missions, or the many rules they had to follow. Many of the soldiers treated the indians badly.	Some soldiers did not like the missions because the work was demanding and they had little pay.
Settlers	Most east Many Settlers were excited to start a new life. But, they had little money.	Some pueblo settlers viewed the indians as laborers.
California Indians	Some of the indians like the mission, and others don't. Some of them don't like the	I know because there was a indian who learned to read and write, and he wrote about how the indians felt. His point of view was

Hello Hello

they helping the indians by teaching them the Catholic Religion

mission because they thought it took away their freedom.

that he thought the indians liked the missions.

Report / Your Findings

Think About It

Make Inferences

Review your research. Based on the information you have gathered, what experiences do you think might have caused California Indians to rebel against the missions?

Write About It

Take a Stand

Write and Cite Evidence Write a speech that a California Indian could have presented to persuade others to rebel against the missions. Include facts and details that support your argument.

_____

_____

_____

_____

_____

_____

_____

_____

_____

_____

_____

_____

_____

_____

Talk About It

Expand

With a partner, discuss what a missionary or Spanish soldier might have thought about your speech. How might the point of view of a missionary or Spanish soldier be different from that of a California Indian?

 History

Connect to the

Pull It Together

What do you think the California Indians hoped to change by rebelling against the missions?

_____

_____

_____

_____

_____

_____

_____

_____

Inquiry Project Notes

_____

_____

_____

_____

_____

_____

What Caused the Mexican War for Independence?

Lesson Outcomes

What Am I Learning?

In this lesson, you're going to use your investigative skills to explore the causes and results of the Mexican War for Independence.

Why Am I Learning It?

Reading and talking about how the war started and the results of the war will help you understand the war's impact on California.

How Will I Know That I Learned It?

You will be able to explain what caused the Mexican War for Independence and how the war affected the people of California.

Talk About It COLLABORATE

Examine Look again at the mural, caption, and text. In the mural, what event is taking place? How do the speaker's face and raised arms reveal his emotions?

HSS.4.2.7, HSS.4.2.8; HAS.HI.3

McGraw-Hill Education

In this detail from *The Cry of Dolores* mural, Father Miguel Hidalgo speaks to his people.

Father Miguel Hidalgo cared deeply about the people born in New Spain and thought they were being treated unfairly by Spanish rule. On September 16, 1810, Father Hidalgo gave an historic speech called the "Cry of Dolores."

There is no record of his exact words, but his speech convinced many of the colonists to go to war for independence from Spain. A long and bloody war began. The war lasted eleven years, ending in 1821.

1 Inspect

Look Examine the territory maps carefully. Think about how control of the area changed over time.

- **Label** the areas controlled by Spain or Mexico on each map.
  - Write an **S** on areas controlled by Spain.
  - Write an **M** on areas controlled by Mexico.
- **Underline** information in the titles, labels and map keys that helps you understand the events that happened in Mexico. Underline any dates you see, too.

My Notes

_____

_____

_____

_____

_____

_____

_____

_____

_____

_____

New Spain, 1810

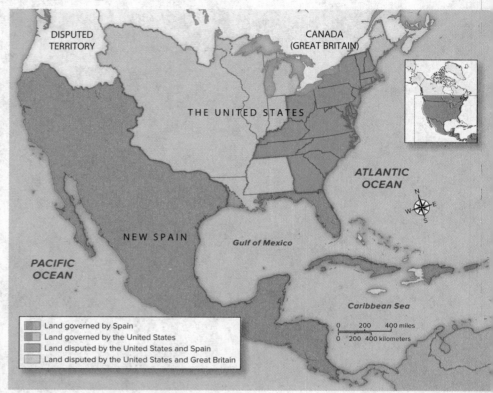

Land governed by Spain
Land governed by the United States
Land disputed by the United States and Spain
Land disputed by the United States and Great Britain

Maps have many purposes, including showing historical changes in an area. Some changes become clear when you look at the colors on maps, which often show the boundaries of countries, states, territories, and more.

Examine the map above, which shows how much land Spain controlled in 1810. Think about some of the key facts about New Spain, based on this map.

Mexico, 1824

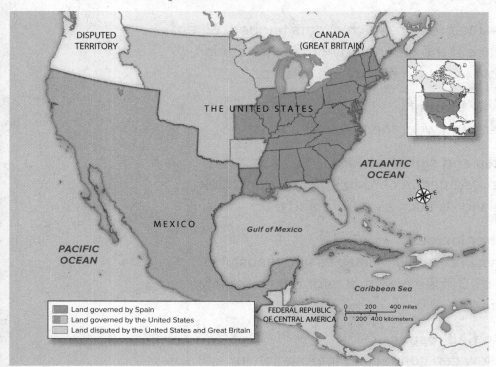

DISPUTED TERRITORY

CANADA (GREAT BRITAIN)

THE UNITED STATES

ATLANTIC OCEAN

MEXICO

Gulf of Mexico

PACIFIC OCEAN

Caribbean Sea

FEDERAL REPUBLIC OF CENTRAL AMERICA

N W E S

0 200 400 miles
0 200 400 kilometers

Land governed by Spain
Land governed by the United States
Land disputed by the United States and Great Britain

Look Again What does the 1824 map show about changes in land control from 1810? What do these changes suggest about the new government of Mexico? How can you tell that Spain was defeated in the Mexican War for Independence? Use details in the map to cite evidence.

Look again at the colors and labels on this map. They show the borders created by Mexico's 1824 constitution, after the War for Independence. You can see that in 1824, control of the area was quite different. Much of the land that had been controlled by Spain came under Mexico's control. Neither Spain nor Mexico controlled some parts of what once had been New Spain.

3 Make Connections

Talk With a partner, discuss the two maps.

COLLABORATE

What does the map of 1810 tell you? Compare the two maps. What similarities do you see? What are some differences?

McGraw-Hill Education

Explore Chronology

Chronology is time order—the order in which events happen. When you examine a text, think about the chronology of the information to help you understand how events in history are related.

1. **Read the text all the way through.**
   This will help you understand what the text is about.

2. **Watch for specific dates and signal words.**
   Are events in the text presented in chronological order? Look for dates and for signal words such as *before* and *after*.

3. **Examine maps and other images.**
   Read the titles, captions, and labels of images and maps. Are any key facts presented? Decide how that information fits into the chronology of the text.

4. **Connect information to find results.**
   Review the key facts. How can connecting information in chronological order help you understand which information is a result of the Mexican War for Independence?

 COLLABORATE Based on the text you read, work with your class to complete the chart below.

Event	Date	Result
Father Hidalgo gives the "Cry of Dolores" Speech	1810	Many people decided to follow his call and fight for independence from Spain.

Investigate!

Read pages 128–135 in your Research Companion. Use your investigative skills to identify the chronology of events that shows why the Mexican War for Independence happened and how the war affected the people living in California. Use the chart to organize information.

Event	Date	Result
The Mexican War for independence ends.	1821	The new country of Mexico was divided into states and territories.
Mexico becomes a federal republic	1824	The new government declared that all the people of Mexico are equal..
Land grants are supposed to be awarded to ~~Mexican citizens living in CA.~~ California Indians	1834	Most of the mission land went to Californios and to Presidio soldiers.

Think About It

Review Your Research

Review your research. What do you think was the most important cause and the most important consequence of the Mexican War for Independence?

Write About It

Write and Explain

Write a paragraph about the Mexican War for Independence. Explain what caused the war between Mexico and Spain and how Mexican independence affected California.

Talk About It

Defend Your Explanation

Read your explanation to a partner and listen to your partner's explanation. Ask each other questions about the effects of Mexico's independence on California. Discuss your answers. For questions you cannot answer, discuss what resources you might use to find answers.

History

Connect to the

Pull It Together

Think about what you read and the maps you studied in this lesson. How did the Mexican War for Independence affect California?

_____

_____

_____

_____

_____

_____

_____

Inquiry Project Notes

_____

_____

_____

_____

_____

_____

_____

How Did Ranchos Transform California?

Lesson Outcomes

What Am I Learning?

In this lesson, you're going to use your investigative skills to explore how missions became ranchos in California.

Why Am I Learning It?

Reading and talking about how missions became ranchos will help you understand the ranchos' effect on California's economy and people.

How Will I Know That I Learned It?

You will be able to explain what led to the system of ranchos and how ranchos changed California.

Talk About It

Inspect Look closely at the picture. How would you describe the land? For what do you think the land could be used?

HSS.4.2.5, HSS.4.2.8; HAS.CS.3, HAS.HI.2, HAS.HR.2

Juana Briones (1802–1889) was one of the first rancheras, or women, who owned a rancho in her own name. She was born in Santa Cruz. Later, she became a founder of the city of San Francisco.

Analyze the Source

1 Inspect

Read Look at the title. What is a land grant?

- **Circle** words and phrases that help you understand the meaning of *land grant*.
- **Highlight** in the chart the name of the owner who received the largest land grant.
- **Discuss** with a partner how the chart supports information in the text.

My Notes

_____

_____

_____

_____

_____

_____

_____

_____

_____

_____

_____

_____

_____

Who Received Land Grants?

The Mexican government took over the mission lands from Spain. The land was supposed to **revert**, or be returned to the California Indians. Instead, after Governor Figueroa died in 1835, a committee took over the distribution. The committee gave most of the land to well-to-do Mexican citizens. The San Francisco Bay area was home to the largest land parcels. When Mission San Francisco closed, it freed up 300,000 acres. In the end, the committee gave only a few land titles to California Indians.

Read the column headings. Then, find the first name in the left column. Look to the right to see the figure that goes with the name. Read down the chart. In what order is the chart organized?

The Mexican landowners took livestock and tools from the missions. These large estates required a labor system to survive. Cattle and land needed care. The landowners and their families needed help. California Indians became the laborers on ranchos, just as they had provided labor to the missionaries and soldiers at the missions. The California Indians depended on the landowners, exchanging their labor for food and clothing.

Largest Land Grants in Mexican California

Names of Owners	Acres Received
de la Guerra family	326,000
Yorba family	235,000
Abel Stearns	200,000
Carrillo family	165,000
Pío and Andres Pico	142,000
Juan Bandini	130,000
Castro family	120,000
Arguello family	116,000
Lugo family	100,000
Estrada family	66,000
Ortega family	44,000
Estudillo family	35,000

2 Find Evidence

Reread What is the purpose of the chart? What idea does it support? How would you explain why no California Indian names appear in the chart?

Reread the statement, "The Mexican government took over the mission lands from Spain. The land was supposed to revert, or be returned to, the California Indians." What does the word *revert* mean?

3 Make Connections

Talk Discuss with COLLABORATE a partner reasons why owners of ranchos needed so many workers on their land.

Discuss if the role of California Indians was the same, or different, from their role in the missions.

Explore Main Idea and Key Details

The **main idea** is the most important idea that a writer presents in a text. **Key details** give important information to support the main idea.

1. **Read the text from beginning to end.**
   This gives you a complete overview of the material.

2. **Identify the key details.**
   Then figure out what the key details have in common.
   Highlight them.

3. **Use key details to determine the main idea of each section of the text.**
   Ask yourself, "What can I conclude from these details?"
   Underline the main ideas of each section.

4. **Summarize the main ideas.**
   Write one or two sentences that summarize each main idea of the text.

 Based on the text you read, work with your class to complete the concept web below.

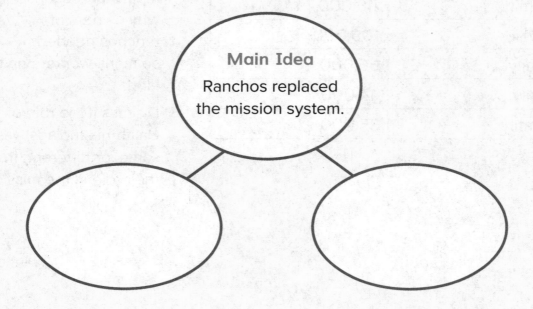

Main Idea

Ranchos replaced the mission system.

Investigate!

Read pages 136–145 in your Research Companion. Use your investigative skills to identify key details that tell how ranchos changed the lives of people and the economy.

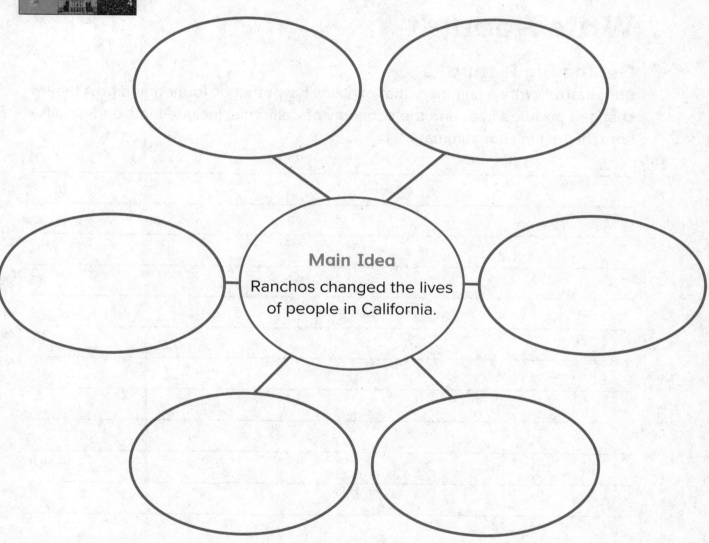

Main Idea
Ranchos changed the lives of people in California.

Think About It

Review Your Research
Review your research. How did life in California change when Mexico closed the missions and gave land grants to Californios?

Write About It

Get the Big Picture
Summarize Write a summary that explains how ranchos formed and how they changed people's lives and the economy of California. Include facts and details from the text in your summary.

_____

_____

_____

_____

_____

_____

_____

_____

_____

_____

_____

_____

_____

_____

_____

_____

_____

_____

Talk About It

Comprehend

Take turns reading your summary to a partner. Repeat what your partner says in your own words. Be sure to include details that tell how California's economy changed after the missions closed and the ranchos started. Next, discuss the economies of ranchos and missions.

Economics

Connect to the

The Main Idea

Write about how ranchos changed California.

_____

_____

_____

_____

_____

_____

_____

_____

Inquiry Project Notes

_____

_____

_____

_____

_____

_____

Lesson 4

Why Did People Move to California?

Lesson Outcomes

What Am I Learning?
In this lesson, you're going to use your investigative skills to understand why people risked their lives to move to California.

Why Am I Learning It?
Reading and talking about resources that attracted people to California will help you understand why people came.

How Will I Know That I Learned It?
You will be able to explain how the desire to make a new life in California outweighed the dangers of traveling across the country.

Talk About It

Examine Look closely at the picture. Where are these people? What is the relationship between the people in the wagons and the American Indians? How do you know?

HSS.4.3.1, HSS.4.3.2; HAS.CS.5; HAS.HR.2; HAS.HI.1, HAS.HI.4

McGraw-Hill Education

Wagon trains crossed the Great Plains on their way to California.

Life Before the Gold Rush

Johann Sutter built a settlement near San Francisco. It was a first welcome stop to many pioneers. Sutter helped pioneers recover after their long travels. He also helped them find jobs and get settled. John Bidwell led a party of **pioneers** across the country. After coming to Sutter's settlement, Bidwell and Sutter became close friends.

PRIMARY SOURCE

In Their Words...
excerpt by John Bidwell

It was wet when we started, and much of the time we traveled through a pouring rain. Streams were out of their banks; gulches were swimming; plains were inundated; indeed, most of the country was overflowed....We got out of provisions and were about three days without food. "Game was plentiful but hard to shoot in the rain." Besides, it was impossible to keep our old flint-lock guns dry, and especially the powder dry in the pans. On the eighth day we came to Sutter's settlement; the fort had not then been begun. Sutter received us with open arms and in a princely fashion, for he was a man of the most polite address and the most courteous manners, a man who could shine in a society.

—from "*Life in California Before the Gold Discovery,*" *The Century Magazine*, December, 1890.

TEXT: Bidwell, John. "Life in California Before the Gold Discovery." *The Century Magazine* 41, no. 3 (December 1890).

Like many pioneers, Bidwell risked his life to come to California. These new settlers came mostly from states in the East. When Bidwell arrived in California, Sutter offered him a job. Years later, Bidwell became a Mexican citizen, like many other settlers at that time. After gaining citizenship, Bidwell obtained a land grant. It was a 22,000-acre ranch near Sacramento.

2 Find Evidence

Reread What does the text suggest about the difficulties of traveling to California? What details support your answer?

In what ways did Sutter help Bidwell? Give details from the text that support your answer.

3 Make Connections

Talk How did Bidwell describe Johann Sutter? How did Sutter help settlers?

COLLABORATE

Explore Making Inferences

Inferences are conclusions that are not stated directly but are based on evidence. To make inferences, readers put together details from the text. Then, they connect the details to what they already know. To make an inference is to figure out information not stated directly.

1. **Look for details in the reading.**
   What details can you find? Together, what could they mean?

2. **Add the clues to what you already know.**
   What do you already know that you can connect to the clues?

3. **Make an inference.**
   What can you infer based on the clues and what you already know?

 COLLABORATE Based on the text you read, work with your class to complete the chart below.

Text Clues	What You Already Know	Inference
Flooding, only paths to follow, ran out of provisions, gun powder was too wet to use to shoot game		

Investigate!

Read pages 146–153 in your Research Companion. Use your investigative skills to identify an inference you can make from text clues that tell you why people wanted to come to California. Use the chart to organize information.

Text Clues	What You Already Know	Inference

Think About It

Make Inferences
What caused many people to move to California in the early 1800s?

Write About It

Create a Diary or Journal Entry
Write Historical Fiction Imagine you are a pioneer heading to California. Write a diary entry that tells why you are moving to California, describe your journey, and explain how you plan to make a living.

_____

_____

_____

_____

_____

_____

_____

_____

_____

_____

_____

_____

_____

_____

_____

Talk About It

Share

Exchange diary entries with a classmate. Read your classmate's entry and discuss which details in the writing are most vivid and engaging and why.

History

Connect to the

Pull It Together

Who came to California in the early 1800s? Why did they come? Make a list.

_____

_____

_____

_____

_____

_____

_____

_____

_____

_____

_____

Inquiry Project Notes

_____

_____

_____

_____

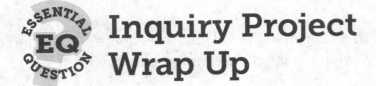

Inquiry Project Wrap Up

Write with a Point of View

Now's the time for you to share your story with the rest of the class. Here's what to do.

Use your story to present a point of view that tells how California changed during Mexican rule.

☐ Share your story plan. Talk about why you chose the person or event.

☐ Include facts, quotes, and details in your story that reveal your point of view.

☐ Answer questions from others about the point of view presented.

Tips for Presenting Point of View

Remember these tips when you present to your class.

☐ Practice reading aloud your story.

☐ Practice incorporating technology, such as a slide show presentation.

☐ Read with expression to engage your audience and emphasize the point of view.

☐ Speak clearly at an understandable pace.

Project Rubric

Use these questions to help evaluate your project.

	Yes	No
Did I base my story on the time period when Mexico ruled California?		
Did I use facts and details to support what my historical figure's point of view could have been?		
Did I create a plan to organize my story?		
Did I tell about a conflict and resolution?		
Did I use words from the chapter vocabulary?		
Did I ask my audience for feedback?		

Project Reflection

Think about the story that you wrote. Describe something you think you did very well. In what areas would you like to improve? Can you think of other ways to incorporate technology into your presentation?

_____

_____

_____

_____

McGraw-Hill Education

Chapter 4

The Golden State

ESSENTIAL EQ QUESTION

What Early Events and People Defined the State of California?

In this chapter, you'll read about how California changed between the years of 1845 and 1851. You'll explore the events and people that caused these changes.

Talk About It

COLLABORATE

Discuss with a partner questions you have about what California was like under Mexican rule and how California changed when it joined the United States. As you research the events and people that defined California as a state, look for answers to your questions. Let's get started!

My Research Questions

1. _____

_____

2. _____

_____

3. _____

_____

Inquiry Project

Time Line of People and Events in California 1845–1851

In this project you'll work with a team to create a time line poster that shows the events and people who made great changes to California during the period of 1845 to 1851.

Here's your project checklist.

☐ **Discuss** with your group which people and events to include on the time line.

☐ **Decide** who will research which person or event. Each team member will have an assignment.

☐ **Research** your person or event and their importance to California's growth. To guide your research, write a list of questions you want to answer.

☐ **Analyze** your research, and select the information you would like to include on your section of the time line.

☐ **Discuss** your person or event with your team. Explain what you would like to include on the time line, and support your opinions with evidence.

☐ **Create** captions and visuals to make your section interesting and easy to understand.

Explore Words

Complete this chapter's Word Rater.
Write notes as you learn more about each word.

amendment
- ☐ Know It!
- ☐ Heard It!
- ☐ Don't Know It!

My Notes
_____
_____
_____

boomtown
- ☐ Know It!
- ☐ Heard It!
- ☐ Don't Know It!

My Notes
_____
_____
_____

claim
- ☐ Know It!
- ☐ Heard It!
- ☐ Don't Know It!

My Notes
_____
_____
_____

compromise
- ☐ Know It!
- ☐ Heard It!
- ☐ Don't Know It!

My Notes
_____
_____
_____

constitution
- ☐ Know It!
- ☐ Heard It!
- ☐ Don't Know It!

My Notes
_____
_____
_____

delegates

☐ Know It!
☐ Heard It!
☐ Don't Know It!

My Notes

_____

_____

_____

Manifest Destiny

☐ Know It!
☐ Heard It!
☐ Don't Know It!

My Notes

_____

_____

_____

republic

☐ Know It!
☐ Heard It!
☐ Don't Know It!

My Notes

_____

_____

_____

treaty

☐ Know It!
☐ Heard It!
☐ Don't Know It!

My Notes

_____

_____

_____

Lesson Outcomes

What Am I Learning?

In this lesson, you are going to use your investigative skills to explore how California became part of the United States.

Why Am I Learning It?

Reading and talking about how California became a state will help you better understand the state of California as it is today. You will also learn about the reasons for the American expansion westward to the Pacific.

How Will I Know That I Learned It?

You will be able to identify the chronology of events leading up to the addition of California to the United States. You will be able to state an opinion about the process of American expansion into California. You will also be able to support your opinion with evidence.

Talk About It

COLLABORATE

Inspect Look at the picture. What is happening? What do you learn about the time period? Read the text. What idea does it express? How might it connect to the picture?

HSS.4.3.5; HAS.CS.1, HAS.CS.2, HAS.HR.2, HAS.HI.1

McGraw-Hill Education

soldiers fighting in the Mexican-American War, 1846–1948

Prints and Photographs Division, Library of Congress, LC-USZC4-2660
TEXT:Gilpin, William. *The Central Gold Region. The Grain, Pastoral, and Gold Regions of North America....* Philadelphia: J. B. Lippincott & Co., 1873.

PRIMARY SOURCE

In Their Words... William Gilpin

"The . . . destiny of the American people is to subdue the continent—to rush over this vast field to the Pacific Ocean—to animate the many hundred millions of its people, and to cheer them upward—to set the principle of self-government at work . . . to set free the enslaved . . . to teach old nations a new civilization—to confirm the destiny of the human race . . . to dissolve the spell of tyranny and exalt charity—to absolve the curse that weighs down humanity, and to shed blessings round the world!"

—*From an address to the U.S. Senate, March 2, 1846*

1 Inspect

Read Look at the title. What do you think this text will be about?

- **Circle** words you don't know.
- **Underline** clues that help you answer these questions: "Why did Americans want to settle in the West? How did their wants conflict with those of the inhabitants?"
- **Discuss** with a partner what the term Manifest Destiny means and what role this concept played in the conflict.

My Notes

_____

_____

_____

_____

_____

_____

_____

_____

_____

_____

Manifest Destiny

In the early 1800s, people from the United States traveled westward and settled in territories. They could claim land to farm and to build a house on. Some of these territories belonged to the United States, but some belonged to Mexico. American Indians lived in all of the territories. To many people already living there, the American settlers seemed like intruders.

Many Americans believed that it was the *destiny*, or fate, of the United States to occupy the land between the Atlantic and Pacific Oceans. They believed that this destiny was *manifest*, or obvious. This belief was called **Manifest Destiny**. People who believed in Manifest Destiny thought that the United States had the right to take the land because they were meant to have it and because they were bringing a better way of life to the people there.

On March 2, 1846, William Gilpin addressed the United States Senate. Gilpin was an advisor to President Polk and a passionate believer in Manifest Destiny. He hoped to win the U.S. Senate members over to the cause. Reread his words on page 141.

At this time, the U.S. did not own land all the way west to the Pacific. Mexico and the U.S. shared a border, but it was not stable. Mexico and the Republic of Texas were already disputing land north of the Rio Grande.

MAP KEY

Land governed by Mexico
Land governed by the United States
Land governed by the Republic of Texas
Land disputed by Mexico and the Republic of Texas
Land disputed by Arkansas and the Republic of Texas

CANADA
(GREAT BRITAIN)

OREGON COUNTRY
(SHARED WITH
GREAT BRITAIN)

Snake River

Missouri River

Mississippi River

THE UNITED STATES

Great
Salt Lake

Platte River

Colorado River

Ohio River

MEXICO

Arkansas River

Tennessee River

DISPUTED
AREA
(MEXICO AND TEXAS)

Red River

Gila River

Rio Grande

REPUBLIC
OF
TEXAS

ATLANTIC
OCEAN

PACIFIC
OCEAN

Gulf of Mexico

0   200   400 miles
0 200   400 kilometers

The United States, 1844

2 Find Evidence

Reread How do the words of William Gilpin on page 141 help you understand Manifest Destiny? What do you think Gilpin is talking about when he says, "to animate the many hundred millions of its people, and to cheer them upward—to set the principle of self-government at work"?

Reread What does the word *subdue* mean? What is another word that has the same meaning?

3 Make Connections

Talk Discuss with a partner why people who believed in Manifest Destiny thought that the United States had a right to take over the western territories.

Discuss reasons other people might have had for disagreeing with Manifest Destiny.

Explore Main Idea and Key Details

Finding the main idea and key details in a text can help you to better understand what you are reading. The main idea is the most important idea that a writer presents in a text or part of a text. Key details give important information that support the main idea.

1. **Read the text once all the way through.**
   This will help you understand what the text is about.

2. **Look at headings, quotations, and images.**
   Does the heading help you identify the main idea? Is there a quote or an image that supports what you're reading about?

3. **Identify the key details.**
   Underline details that help you understand westward expansion and the concept of Manifest Destiny.

4. **Find out what the key details have in common.**
   How are the details connected? This will help you figure out the main idea of a section.

 COLLABORATE Based on the text you read, work with your class to complete the chart below.

Main Idea	Details
The United States believed in Manifest Destiny.	

Investigate!

Read pages 162–169 in your Research Companion. Use your investigative skills to identify the main ideas and supporting details of each section. Use the chart to organize information.

Main Idea	Details

Main Idea	Details

Think About It

Review Your Research

Based on the information you have gathered, do you agree with the principles of Manifest Destiny? Why or why not?

Write About It

Take a Stand

Write and Cite Evidence Write an editorial that explains your opinion about the United States going to war with Mexico to gain western lands. Include your opinions about the events that led to California becoming part of the United States. Support your opinions with facts and details from the text.

_____

_____

_____

_____

_____

_____

_____

_____

_____

_____

_____

_____

_____

_____

_____

Talk About It

Defend Your Position

Read your editorial aloud to a partner. Discuss the facts and details that you think best support your opinion. Are there any other reasons you can think of that support your position?

History

Connect to the

Pull It Together

How did the Mexican War and the Bear Flag Revolt affect California in the past and for present and future generations?

_____

_____

_____

_____

Inquiry Project Notes

_____

_____

_____

_____

_____

_____

_____

_____

How Did the Gold Rush Change California?

Lesson Outcomes

What Am I Learning?

In this lesson, you're going to use your investigative skills to understand how the Gold Rush changed California.

Why Am I Learning it?

Reading and talking about the people and events of the Gold Rush will help you understand how the Gold Rush had a lasting effect on the settlements, daily life, politics, and environment of California.

How Will I Know That I Learned It?

You will be able to explain some of the ways women and various ethnic groups changed California during the time of the Gold Rush.

Talk About It

Look closely Examine the photographs. Who do you think these people are? When and where do you think these photos were taken? Why do you think so?

HSS.4.3.2, HSS.4.3.3, HSS.4.3.4, HSS.4.4.2; HAS.CS.2, HAS.HR.1, HAS.HR.2, HAS.HI.2, HAS.HI.4

The Gold Rush brought a diverse population to California.

TEXT:Louise Amelia Knapp Smith Clappe. The Shirley Letters From California Mines in 1851-52 Being a Series of Twenty-Three Letters from Dame Shirley (Mrs. Louise Amelia Knapp Smith Clappe) to her Sister in Massachusetts and now Reprinted from the Pioneer Magazine of 1854-55. San Francisco: Thomas C. Russell, 1922.

The Letters of "Dame Shirley"

Louise Clappe came to California in 1849 with her husband, Fayette. They lived in the mining camps, where Fayette worked as a doctor. They also searched for gold. Louise Clappe wrote twenty-three colorful letters to her sister Molly in Massachusetts. The letters were later published in *Pioneer* magazine. Clappe described life in the mining camps and signed her letters as "Dame Shirley." Her letters help us understand the daily life of the miners, who were called "forty-niners."

PRIMARY SOURCE

In Their Words... "Dame Shirley"

RICH BAR, EAST BRANCH of the NORTH FORK of FEATHER RIVER

September 20, 1851

". . . Through the middle of Rich Bar runs the street, thickly planted with about forty tenements, among which figure round tents, square tents, plank hovels, log cabins, etc. ... I was introduced to one of the finders of Rich Bar,—a young Georgian,—who afterwards gave me a full description of all the facts connected with its discovery. This unfortunate had not spoken to a woman for two years, ... Mr. H. informed me that on the 20th of July, 1850, it was rumored at

1 Inspect

Read Find information about Louise Clappe and her letter as Dame Shirley. When and where was the letter written?

- **Underline** clues that help you answer these questions:
  - Who is Louise Clappe?
  - What main event does she tell about in her letter?
  - What is the effect?
- **Discuss** with a partner how the letter helps you understand life among the miners.

My Notes

_____

_____

_____

_____

_____

_____

_____

_____

_____

Nelson's Creek—a mining station ... —that ... [somebody] had discovered mines of a remarkable richness.... A large company packed up their goods and chattels, generally consisting of a pair of blankets, a frying-pan, some flour, salt pork, brandy, pickax and shovel, and started for the new Dorado. They "traveled, and traveled, and traveled," as we used to say in the fairy-stories, for nearly a week, in every possible direction, when, one evening, weary and discouraged, about one hundred of the party found themselves at the top of that famous hill which figures so largely in my letters, whence the river can be distinctly seen. Half of the number concluded to descend the mountain that night, the remainder stopping on the summit until the next morning. On arriving at Rich Bar, part of the adventurers camped there, but many went a few miles farther down the river. The next morning, two men turned over a large stone, beneath which they found quite a sizable piece of gold. They washed a small panful of the dirt, and obtained from it two hundred and fifty-six dollars. Encouraged by this success, they commenced staking off the legal amount of ground allowed to each person for mining purposes, and, the remainder of the party having descended the hill, before night the entire bar was "claimed."

—Reprinted from *The Pioneer*, April 1854.

McGraw-Hill Education

2 Find Evidence

Reread Notice the details given in the letter about Rich Bar. How does Clappe describe life in the gold mining camp of Rich Bar?

How is information from a firsthand account different from other sources of information?

Reread her description about the discovery of gold. What does the word *chattel* mean? Name a word that has almost the same meaning.

Why do you suppose "Dame Shirley" tells her sister about chattels?

3 Make Connections

Talk With a partner, discuss the events that "Dame Shirley" describes. Point out some of the interesting words that she uses. What opinions does she seem to have about life among the miners?

COLLABORATE

Explore Cause and Effect

A **cause** is why something happens. An **effect** is the result of what happens. An event can be either a cause or an effect.

To find a cause and its effect:

1. **Read the text all the way through.**
   This will help you understand what the text is about.

2. **Reread the text and look for a detail that tells you what or why something happened.**
   This is a cause. Circle it.

3. **Reread the text again and look for a detail that tells you the result of what happened.**
   This is the effect. Underline it.

4. **Finish the cause-and-effect statement.**
   Because of _____, the result was _____.

COLLABORATE Based on the text you read, work with your class to complete the chart below.

Cause	Effect
Two men found a sizeable piece of gold.	
It was rumored that gold was found at Nelson's Creek.	

Investigate!

Read pages 170–179 in your Research Companion. Use your investigative skills to identify causes and effects of the Gold Rush that affected California's population, economy, and environment.

Cause	Effect

Think About It

Review Your Research

How did life in California change during the Gold Rush?

Write About It

Present a Conflict

Write and Cite Evidence Write a script for a short play. In your play, show what life was like in a mining camp. Base events or conflicts on something that really might have happened.

_____

_____

_____

_____

_____

_____

_____

_____

_____

_____

_____

_____

_____

_____

_____

Talk About It

Compare and Contrast

Exchange scripts with a classmate. Compare and contrast events or conflicts. Discuss how you might rewrite scripts, including solutions to conflicts.

History

Connect to the

Pull It Together

How did the Gold Rush change the population and environment of California?

_____

_____

_____

_____

_____

_____

_____

_____

_____

Inquiry Project Notes

_____

_____

_____

_____

_____

Why Is It Important That California Became a State?

Lesson Outcomes

What Am I Learning?

In this lesson, you are going to use your investigative skills to explore the important issues that led to California becoming a state.

Why Am I Learning It?

Reading and talking about these issues will help you understand the importance of California becoming a state.

How Will I Know That I Learned It?

You will be able to identify the events leading up to California becoming a state, explain why the issue of slavery was so important, and compare California's new government to previous Spanish and Mexican governments.

Talk About It

COLLABORATE

Look at the document. What do you know about the Constitution of the United States? How do you think a state constitution might be the same? What might be different?

HSS.4.3.4, HSS.4.3.5, HSS.4.5.2; HAS.CS.1, HAS.HR.1, HAS.HI.1

156 Lesson 3 Why Is It Important That California Became a State?

McGraw-Hill Education

The Constitution of California was written in 1849.

Read Look at the title. What does the word *government* mean to you?

- **Circle** words and phrases you don't know.
- **Underline** words or phrases that help you understand the meanings of new words.
- **Highlight** important events and facts.

My Notes

_____

_____

_____

_____

_____

_____

_____

_____

_____

_____

_____

_____

_____

_____

A Call for New Government

California's path toward statehood began after the Mexican War and the discovery of gold. After the war, California was part of the United States, but it was not a state. The United States Congress of 1848 and 1849 took no action to set up the government as either a territory or a state.

The Gold Rush brought many people to California. Californians wanted to make their own laws. They could not vote or choose their leaders. Instead, military governors were appointed. Because there was no court system, people in mining camps and towns were making up their own laws. California had reached a turning point.

General Bennett F. Riley, the last military governor, took action. On June 3, 1849, he called for an election of **delegates**. Delegates would represent the people. They would write a plan for government, a **constitution**. After being in session for forty-three days, the delegates adopted a constitution for California.

(t)McGraw-Hill Education; TEXT:Report of the Debates in the Convention of California, on the Formation of the State Constitution, in September and October, 1849. By J. Ross Browne. Washington, 1850.

In Their Words...
General Bennett F. Riley

"The people are now called upon to form a government for themselves, and to designate such officers as they desire to make and execute the laws. That their choice may be wisely made, and that the government so organized may secure the permanent welfare and happiness of the people of the new State, is the sincere and earnest wish of the present Executive, who, if the Constitution be ratified, will, with pleasure, surrender his powers to whomsoever the people may designate as his successor."

—October 12, 1849, proclamation to the people of California

2 Find Evidence

Reread How do you think General Riley feels about making this proclamation? What words does he use to let you know how he feels about his role in the new government?

What words or phrases tell you the purpose of the constitution?

3 Make Connections

Talk Discuss with a partner why California needed a constitution. Give reasons based on text evidence.

COLLABORATE

Explore Chronology

Putting events in order while you read, or identifying the **chronology**, will help you understand the relationship between events.

1. **Read the text once all the way through.**
   To get an overall sense of what a text is about, read it all the way through without stopping.

2. **Reread a second time.**
   Ask yourself questions as you read a second time.

3. **Notice how the text is organized.**
   Look for clues that tell time order. Do you see dates or time order words such as *first*, *second*, *then*, *after*, or *finally*?

4. **Look at text features.**
   Do text features, such as headings, photos, or time lines, help you put events in order?

5. **Identify the most important events.**
   While reading, ask yourself what key facts about each event show that it was important to California becoming a state.

 COLLABORATE   Based on the text you read, work with your class to complete the chart below.

Event:
Key Facts:

↓

Event:
Key Fact:

Investigate!

Read pages 180–189 in your Research Companion. Use your investigative skills to identify the chronology of events that led to California becoming a state. Use the chart to organize information.

Event:

Key Facts:

⬇

Event:

Key Facts:

⬇

Event:

Key Facts:

⬇

Event:

Key Facts:

Think About It

Review Your Research

Based on the information you have gathered, what events made it important for California to become a state?

Write About It

Explain

Why was the issue of slavery so important when California joined the United States?

_____

_____

_____

_____

_____

_____

_____

Write and Cite Evidence

List the main concerns each side of the debate had about California joining the United States as a free state. Explain why each concern mattered and whether it was important to the debate. Use text evidence.

_____

_____

_____

_____

_____

_____

_____

Talk About It

Compare

Exchange your work with a classmate. Take turns discussing the concerns you found about the issue of slavery and California's statehood. Did your partner find concerns different from yours?

Civics

Connect to the

Pull It Together

Think about the importance of California becoming a state. What decisions needed to be made? What obstacles were overcome?

_____

_____

_____

_____

_____

_____

_____

_____

_____

Inquiry Project Notes

_____

_____

_____

Inquiry Project Wrap Up

Time Line of People and Events in California 1845–1851

Now's the time for your team to share your time line poster with the rest of the class. Here's what to do.

Use the time line poster to show events and people who brought changes to California from 1845–1851.

☐ Display and explain your time line, pointing out the information or illustrations you included about key people and events.

☐ Defend your information by citing valid text evidence.

☐ Talk about your method for determining which people or events to include on your time line.

Tips for Presenting

Remember these tips when you present to your class.

☐ Practice what you will say and do.

☐ Take turns with members of your team to carry out assigned roles.

☐ Speak clearly and not too quickly or slowly.

☐ Explain captions, illustrations, or visuals.

Project Rubric

Use these questions to help evaluate your project.

	Yes	No
Did I collaborate to meet our goal?		
Did I help conduct research and answer the questions I prepared?		
Did I accomplish my individual assignment and include research about a person or event?		
Did I include media in my research?		

Project Reflection

Think about the time line poster that your team made and what you contributed to it. Describe something you think was successful. Is there anything you would do differently in another project?

_____

_____

_____

_____

_____

_____

Chapter 5

A Growing State

ESSENTIAL EQ QUESTION How Did California Change After Becoming a State?

In this chapter, you'll explore how California connected to the rest of the country. You'll also read about the problem of too little or too much water.

Talk About It COLLABORATE

Discuss with a partner questions you have about how California's immigrants helped to connect it to the rest of the country and how the state solved its problems with water. As you research the people, events, and ideas from these early days of building a state economy, look for answers to your questions. Let's get started!

My Research Questions

1. _____

_____

2. _____

_____

3. _____

_____

EQ Inquiry Project

Our Growing State Photo Album

You will work with a team to create a photo essay that explains changes in the state of California from 1850 to the present. It should look like a photo album. Focus on California's growth in transportation and the effect of immigrant labor on the state. Also include California's efforts to deal with water problems. You will select images to represent these changes. Remember to describe and explain the images with captions.

Here's your project checklist.

☐ **Analyze** the task. Make sure you understand what to do and include.

☐ **List** the topics and people who are important to this part of California's history.

☐ **Research** the events and individuals you think will help you tell the story.

☐ **Gather** images of people or scenes that represent the points of your photo essay.

☐ **Write** captions or paragraphs to describe or explain each image.

☐ **Organize** your images to tell the story of how transportation, immigration, and water developments changed California and its people.

Explore Words

Complete this chapter's Word Rater.
Write notes as you learn more about each word.

aqueduct

My Notes

☐ Know It!

☐ Heard It!

☐ Don't Know It!

_____

_____

_____

communication

My Notes

☐ Know It!

☐ Heard It!

☐ Don't Know It!

_____

_____

_____

deport

My Notes

☐ Know It!

☐ Heard It!

☐ Don't Know It!

_____

_____

_____

discrimination

My Notes

☐ Know It!

☐ Heard It!

☐ Don't Know It!

_____

_____

_____

drought

My Notes

☐ Know It!

☐ Heard It!

☐ Don't Know It!

_____

_____

_____

investor

☐ Know It!
☐ Heard It!
☐ Don't Know It!

My Notes

_____
_____
_____

levee

☐ Know It!
☐ Heard It!
☐ Don't Know It!

My Notes

_____
_____
_____

refrigeration

☐ Know It!
☐ Heard It!
☐ Don't Know It!

My Notes

_____
_____
_____

reservoir

☐ Know It!
☐ Heard It!
☐ Don't Know It!

My Notes

_____
_____
_____

transcontinental

☐ Know It!
☐ Heard It!
☐ Don't Know It!

My Notes

_____
_____
_____

What Role Did the Transportation Revolution Play in the Growth of California?

Lesson Outcomes

What Am I Learning?
In this lesson, you're going to use your investigative skills to learn about the role that transportation played in California.

Why Am I Learning It?
Reading and talking about the transportation revolution will help you learn more about how California grew and changed after becoming a state.

How Will I Know That I Learned It?
You will be able to give examples of how transportation helped California grow.

Talk About It

Look at the poster. What is the poster announcing? When does the Pony Express leave St. Joseph? What other details are explained?

HSS.4.4.1, HSS.4.4.2, HSS.4.4.3, HSS.4.4.4; HAS.CS.1

PONY EXPRESS!

CHANGE OF

TIME!

REDUCED

RATES!

10 Days to San Francisco!

LETTERS

WILL BE RECEIVED AT THE

OFFICE, 84 BROADWAY,

NEW YORK,

Up to **4** P. M. every **TUESDAY**,

AND

Up to **2½** P. M. every **SATURDAY**,

Which will be forwarded to connect with the PONY EXPRESS leaving ST. JOSEPH, Missouri,

Every WEDNESDAY and SATURDAY at 11 P. M.

TELEGRAMS

Sent to Fort Kearney on the mornings of MONDAY and FRIDAY, will connect with **PONY** leaving St. Joseph, WEDNESDAYS and SATURDAYS.

EXPRESS CHARGES.

LETTERS weighing half ounce or under...............$1 00
For every additional half ounce or fraction of an ounce 1 00
In all cases to be enclosed in 10 cent Government Stamped Envelopes,
And all Express CHARGES Pre-paid.

☞ **PONY EXPRESS ENVELOPES** For Sale at our Office.

WELLS, FARGO & CO., Ag'ts.

New York, Ju'y 1, 1861.

Advertisement for Pony Express.

1 Inspect

Read Look at the title. What do you think this article will be about?

- **Circle** words and phrases you don't know.
- **Underline** clues that tell you what those words mean.

My Notes

_____

_____

_____

_____

_____

_____

_____

_____

_____

_____

_____

_____

_____

_____

_____

_____

A Dangerous Job

Transportation is the movement of people and goods. It took a long time to get news, mail, supplies, or people to California from the East. To speed **communication**, stagecoaches began delivering the mail. A stagecoach is a carriage pulled by horses.

"Charley" Parkhurst worked for a stagecoach company called Wells Fargo & Co. Being a stagecoach driver was dangerous and hard work. Drivers had to be tough. Stagecoach companies only hired men who were willing to risk their lives. Parkhurst had a scar, an eye patch, and weathered skin.

Parkhurst was a bold and daring stagecoach driver. Parkhurst navigated many difficult trails. Experienced drivers such as Parkhurst were called "whips." Whips skillfully handled their "six-ups," or six horses. It took strength to steer the horses to safely guide the stagecoach.

Later, people found out that "Charley" Parkhurst was really a woman named Charlotte Parkhurst. Stagecoach companies hired only men. What might be the reasons that Parkhurst lived for many years as a man?

A stagecoach driver had a dangerous job.

stocksnapper/iStock/Getty Images

In Their Words...

"Charley was a great 'whip' and when he pulled into the old Nebraska house with a beautifully equipped 20 passenger Concord coach, drawn by six mustangs, as mettlesome as quarter horses, it was an inspiring scene indeed."

"How deftly he, with his right hand, whirled the belly of the six horse lash around the stock and carefully laid it up on the deck above his head, all unconscious of the onlookers, and as he wrapped the lines around the foothold on the brake, he would hand from the boot, treasure and mail; or, perhaps, some venturesome female who insisted on riding with the driver...."

—First-hand account of Major A. N. Judd to the *Santa Cruz Surf*, October 18, 1917

2 Find Evidence

Reread How does Major A. N. Judd feel about Parkhurst? How do you know? What words does he use to describe Parkhurst?

Reread the first-hand account. What information do you learn about the stagecoach as a method of transportation?

3 Make Connections

Talk Discuss with a partner what stagecoach transportation was like. Why do you think the job was so dangerous?

COLLABORATE

Explore Main Idea and Details

A **main idea** tells a key idea, or something the writer wants you to know. The **details** support the main idea.

To identify a main idea and its details:

1. **Look for a sentence that tells an important idea.**
   Sometimes, but not always, a main idea appears in every paragraph.

2. **Look for words, phrases, or ideas that tell more about a main idea.**
   Details give more information and relate to the same main idea.

COLLABORATE Based on the text you read, work with your class to find a main idea and details about stagecoach driver Charley Parkhurst.

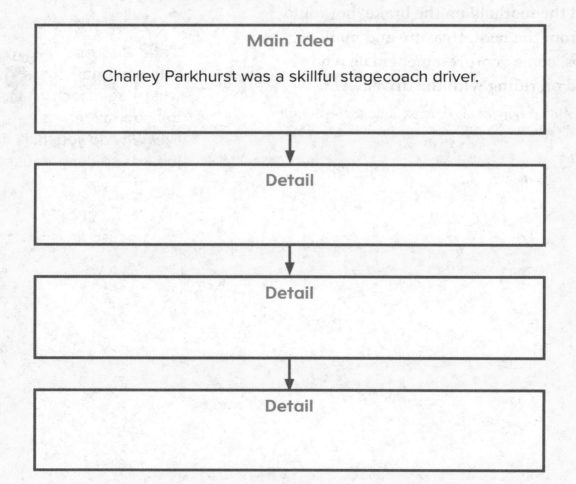

Main Idea
Charley Parkhurst was a skillful stagecoach driver.

↓

Detail

↓

Detail

↓

Detail

Investigate!

Read pages 200–207 in your Research Companion. Use your investigative skills to identify how transportation changed life in California. This chart will help you organize your notes.

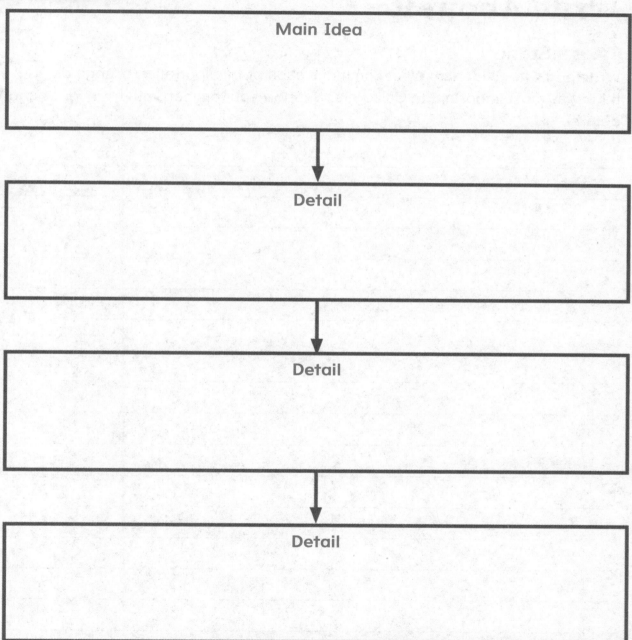

Main Idea

↓

Detail

↓

Detail

↓

Detail

Think About It

Review Your Research

Based on the information you have gathered, what do you think California would be like without improvements in transportation?

Write About It

Take a Stand

Write and Cite Evidence What communication or transportation change do you think was most important to California? Support your opinion with main ideas and details.

_____

_____

_____

_____

_____

_____

_____

_____

_____

_____

_____

_____

_____

_____

Talk About It

Defend Your Claim

Talk with a classmate who chose a different development. Take turns discussing your opinions and citing supporting evidence.

History

Connect to the

Pull it Together

How did transportation change California's population and the economy?

_____

_____

_____

_____

_____

_____

_____

Inquiry Project Notes

_____

_____

_____

_____

_____

_____

Lesson 2

How Were Immigrants to California Treated After the Gold Rush?

Lesson Outcomes

What Am I Learning?

In this lesson, you're going to use your investigative skills to explore what life was like for immigrants after the Gold Rush.

Why Am I Learning It?

Reading and talking about immigrant life will help you learn more about how California developed its unique cultural characteristics.

How Will I Know That I Learned It?

You will be able to explain the major accomplishments of the immigrant communities and the hardships that they faced.

Talk About It

Look closely at the picture. What tasks do you see the workers doing? What are some tools or materials the workers would need to do this work?

HSS.4.4.4

178 Lesson 2 How Were Immigrants to California Treated After the Gold Rush?

McGraw-Hill Education

Most of the workers who built the Transcontinental Railroad were immigrants.

1 Inspect

Read Look at the title. What information do you think the letter will include?

- **Circle** words and phrases you don't know.
- **Underline** language that the writer uses to express his opinion.
- **Discuss** with a partner what Daniel Cleveland thinks about Chinese immigrants to the United States.

My Notes

_____
_____
_____
_____
_____
_____
_____
_____
_____
_____
_____
_____
_____

Excerpt of a Letter from Daniel Cleveland to a friend, February 10, 1869

The following excerpt is from Daniel Cleveland, an attorney and early Californian dedicated to community service, who later served as the director of various railroad lines out of San Diego. In this letter to a friend, he discusses the local debate about Chinese immigration, or "the Chinese Question."

My Dear Friend,

I received your kind letter of Jan'y 12th, a few days ago, and was greatly interested in its contents, informing me as they did of the health of your family, your literary labors, and your purposed change of home.

...I was particularly interested in what you wrote respecting the interest felt in the Chinese Question, as I have been for nearly a year past engaged in writing a work on "the Chinese in California." The collection of material for the work, to say nothing of writing it, has been very difficult and laborious. I propose to consider the Chinese as residents of America, and show how they come, and go, how they live, and what they do, and to review all of the questions in regards to their residence among us.

TEXT: Daniel Cleveland to Benson J. Lossing, 10 February 1869. Online Archives of California.

...The result of my researches into this subject, is the firm conviction that the Chinese are a very valuable addition to our industrial population. They pay in this state alone more than three million dollars in gold, for custom duties and taxes, and contribute more than sixteen millions in gold to sustain our good and benefit our people. They manufacture about one million dollars' worth of cigars and other articles, and I estimate their business and earnings at $22,916,890, in gold per annum.

...Our Chinese New Year season commences today. I will, so soon as I have leisure to arrange them, send you a few Chinese curiosities, such as "marck money", etc.

In November last, I established a mission school for the Chinese in our church, and it has been successful. I now have about 30 scholars. They repeat the Lord's Prayer, sing hymns, and receive religious, as well as secular instruction. It is the most interesting religious work that I have ever engaged in.

...I will be very glad to receive a letter from you, and thus hear of the health and happiness of yourself and family, whenever you have leisure to write.

Your friend,

Daniel Cleveland

McGraw-Hill Education

2 Find Evidence

Reread How might the writer's experiences with Chinese immigrants differ from other Californians?

Reread the statement, "The result of my researches into this subject, is the firm conviction that the Chinese are a very valuable addition to our industrial population." What evidence does the writer provide to support use of the word *valuable*?

Highlight the lines that provide factual information.

3 Make Connections

Talk What view does the letter's author have of Chinese immigrants? How can you tell?

COLLABORATE

Explore Problem/Solution

Texts can be structured around a **problem** and the **solution** to that problem. The beginning of the text will describe the problem. The text that follows will describe a solution. The solution can be something that has already fixed the problem or something the writer is proposing could fix the problem.

To understand problem/solution:

1. **Read the text all the way through.**
   This will help you understand what the text is about.

2. **Look for an issue or problem being described.**
   Are there words that indicate a problem, such as *challenge* or *hardship*?

3. **Identify how the issue is resolved or the challenge overcome.**
   What did the person who was facing the challenge do?

4. **Find a relationship between the solution and the problem.**
   Ask yourself if the person's actions solve the problem described at the beginning.

COLLABORATE Based on the text you read, work with your class to complete the chart below.

Who	Problem	Solution

Investigate!

Read pages 208–219 in your Research Companion. Use your investigative skills to identify evidence that tells you problems that individuals faced and the solutions they found. Use the chart to organize information.

Who	Problem	Solution

Think About It

Review Your Research

Based on the information you have gathered, why is it wrong to discriminate against a group of people?

Write About It

Write and Cite Evidence

What would have been another way to handle the problems that led to the Chinese Exclusion Act? Imagine you were a legislator at that time, and propose an alternative to the act. Cite reasons that support your alternative. Include page references.

_____

_____

_____

_____

_____

_____

_____

_____

_____

_____

_____

_____

_____

_____

_____

Talk About It

Compare

Share your ideas with a partner. Discuss the pros and cons of each other's ideas.

History

Connect to the

How did the population of California change after it became a state? What effect did this have on the people of California and the immigrants who came there to work?

_____

_____

_____

_____

_____

_____

_____

_____

_____

Inquiry Project Notes

_____

_____

_____

_____

_____

How Did California's Growing Population Get Enough Water to Meet Its Needs?

Lesson Outcomes

What Am I Learning?

In this lesson, you're going to use your investigative skills to explore how California helped its growing population get enough water to meet their needs.

Why Am I Learning it?

Reading and talking about how California helped its growing population get enough water will help you learn more about how California changed after it became a state.

How Will I Know That I Learned It?

You will be able to examine problems and solutions with California's water supply. You will be able to support your opinion with evidence about a person's rights and responsibilities regarding water.

Talk About It

COLLABORATE

Look at the Details What do you notice in the pictures? What problems can be caused by a scarce supply of water? What problems can be caused by flooding? How are the pictures alike and different? Whose responsibility is it to deal with these problems?

HSS.4.4.4, HSS.4.4.7

McGraw-Hill Education

Some areas of California have been very dry, while others have flooded from too much rain.

(t)Photo by Tim McCabe, USDA Natural Resources Conservation Service;
(b)Woodward Payne/Photolibrary/Getty Images

1 Inspect

Read Look at the chart. What information does the chart give?

- **Read** the title of the chart and the column headings.
- **Circle** words you don't know.
- **Discuss** with a partner the purpose of the chart.

My Notes

_____

_____

_____

_____

_____

_____

_____

_____

_____

_____

_____

_____

_____

Major California Droughts

Years	Area Affected
1827–1829	Variable
1843–1844	Variable
1856–1857	Variable
1863–1864	Variable
1887–1900	Variable
1912–1913	Variable
1917–1921	Across the state, except central Sierra Nevada and the north coast
1922–1926	Across the state, except central Sierra Nevada
1928–1937	Across the state
1943–1951	Across the state
1959–1962	Across the state
1976–1977	Across the state, except the southwestern deserts
1987–1992	Across the state
2012–2016	Across the state

History of Drought in California

California has experienced several **droughts** since becoming a state. Some have been variable, meaning they affect just parts of the state. Others have affected most of the state. Its history of severe droughts led California to plan and build water projects, including the Central Valley Water Project.

Scientists believe that the drought that began in 2012 is the worst in the state's history. Many people compare this problem to the severe drought of 1976. At that time, rainfall was below normal, the mountains had little snow, and **reservoirs** were low. Another water project was suggested to solve the problem, but it was voted down. Instead, people came up with another solution. They started to conserve, or save, water. For example, many took shorter showers, stopped watering their lawns, and collected rainwater. Farmers also took steps to conserve water by watering their farmland in new and different ways. Today, many people in California are doing these same things to deal with drought.

2 Find Evidence

Reread How does the chart help you understand California's problems with their water supply?

What years did the drought affect most of the state?

Do you think the problem is getting better or worse?

3 Make Connections

Talk Discuss with a partner whether or not you think it is important to conserve water. Talk about ways that you make efforts to conserve water at home or at school.

COLLABORATE

Explore Problem and Solution

A **problem** is an issue that is causing difficulty, trouble, or harm.

A **solution** is something that can be done to fix or overcome a problem.

To find problems and solutions as you read:

1. **Read the text all the way through.**
    This will help you understand what the text is about.

2. **Look for details that tell what the problem is.**
    Look for words that are similar to *problem*, such as *difficulty* and *trouble*. Are there any other signal words that indicate a problem?

3. **Look for details that tell how the problem is solved.**
    Look for words like *solve*, *solution*, and *fix*. Are there any other signal words that indicate a solution?

4. **Make a connection between problems and solutions.**
    Ask yourself, *What problems did California have with its water supply? What solutions did the state come up with to solve these problems?*

COLLABORATE

Based on the text you read, work with your class to complete the problem-and-solution chart below. Find a problem with California's water supply and the solution the state used to solve it.

Problem	Solution

Investigate!

Read pages 220–229 in your Research Companion. Use your investigative skills to identify text evidence that tells you about California's water supply problems and solutions the state came up with to address them. Use the chart to organize your notes.

Problems	Solutions

Think About It

Review Your Research

Who owns water? Whose responsibility is it to be sure communities have enough water to drink, clean, and grow crops?

Write About It

Define

What are water rights?

_____

_____

_____

_____

Write and Cite Evidence

In your opinion, what are a person's rights and responsibilities when it comes to water? List evidence to support your opinion and include page references.

_____

_____

_____

_____

_____

_____

_____

_____

_____

_____

_____

Talk About It

Explain

Share your response with a partner. Compare your thoughts about water rights and responsibilities and include supporting evidence. Do you agree or disagree with your partner's points?

Connect to the

Pull It Together

How did ideas about water change when California became a state and grew in size? Why did the issues surrounding water become so important after California became a state?

_____

_____

_____

_____

_____

Inquiry Project Notes

_____

_____

_____

_____

_____

_____

_____

Inquiry Project Wrap Up

Our Growing State Photo Album

Now's the time for your team to share your photo essay with the rest of the class. Here's what to do.

Present your photo essay to demonstrate how Californians dealt with increased immigration and solved their transportation and water problems.

- ☐ Discuss how the people and places look different from modern California.

- ☐ Point out how the essay helps to tell the story of California.

- ☐ If possible, use videos or online sources to add variety to the presentation.

- ☐ Answer any questions from the audience.

Tips for Presenting

Remember these tips when you present to your class.

- ☐ Read the captions and paragraphs aloud.

- ☐ Ask the audience for their opinions and listen to their responses.

- ☐ Make sure that your audience can see your photo essay.

- ☐ Point out different parts of your pictures and discuss details some audience members may not notice.

Project Rubric

Use these questions to help evaluate your project.

	Yes	No
Did we choose photos that related to the topic?		
Were the chosen photos interesting and informative?		
Were the captions and paragraphs easy to understand and clearly related to the photo essay?		
Was our presentation of the photo essay successful?		
Did the audience react positively to the photo essay?		

Project Reflection

Think about the work you did on your team's photo essay. List the things you'd like to do differently and how you would do that. List the things you were proud of doing and point out why they were successful.

_____

_____

_____

_____

_____

_____

_____

Chapter 6
Californians, Struggling and Working Together

ESSENTIAL EQ QUESTION

How Did Californians Struggle and Work Together During the Difficulties of the 20ᵗʰ Century?

In this chapter, you'll explore the challenges Californians faced in the 1900s. You'll also read about heroic people who improved the lives of others.

COLLABORATE

Talk About It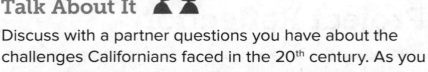

Discuss with a partner questions you have about the challenges Californians faced in the 20ᵗʰ century. As you research people and events, look for answers to your questions. Let's get started!

My Research Questions

1. _____

_____

2. _____

_____

3. _____

_____

Inquiry Project

The Early 20th Century News Show

In this project, you'll work with a team to prepare and produce a ten-minute news show about one of California's struggles of the early 20th century. Model your news segment on a TV news show. Include fictional interviews with people who lived at the time. Present your news show as a play if recording is not possible.

Here's your project checklist.

☐ **List** important events, people, and ideas.

☐ **Focus** your research. Choose one important struggle to explore.

☐ **Assign** people different parts of the task, such as writing, directing, reporting, acting, designing graphics, and recording.

☐ **Write** scripts for reporters and interviews.

☐ **Prepare** visuals, such as photos and illustrations.

☐ **Rehearse** the performance before filming it or presenting it to the class.

☐ **Perform** the news segment for the class. Record the segment to present to parents or post to a class website.

Explore Words

Complete this chapter's Word Rater.
Write notes as you learn more about each word.

boycott

☐ Know It!
☐ Heard It!
☐ Don't Know It!

My Notes

_____
_____
_____

bribe

☐ Know It!
☐ Heard It!
☐ Don't Know It!

My Notes

_____
_____
_____

campus

☐ Know It!
☐ Heard It!
☐ Don't Know It!

My Notes

_____
_____
_____

internment camps

☐ Know It!
☐ Heard It!
☐ Don't Know It!

My Notes

_____
_____
_____

manufacture

☐ Know It!
☐ Heard It!
☐ Don't Know It!

My Notes

_____
_____
_____

public education   My Notes

☐ Know It!   _____

☐ Heard It!   _____

☐ Don't Know It!   _____

reform   My Notes

☐ Know It!   _____

☐ Heard It!   _____

☐ Don't Know It!   _____

segregation   My Notes

☐ Know It!   _____

☐ Heard It!   _____

☐ Don't Know It!   _____

suffrage   My Notes

☐ Know It!   _____

☐ Heard It!   _____

☐ Don't Know It!   _____

World War II   My Notes

☐ Know It!   _____

☐ Heard It!   _____

☐ Don't Know It!   _____

Lesson Outcomes

What Am I Learning?

In this lesson, you're going to use your investigative skills to explore important events that affected California in the early 1900s.

Why Am I Learning It?

Reading and talking about these events will help you understand the long-lasting effects of these events on the state of California.

How Will I Know That I Learned It?

You will be able to identify causes and effects and create a time line of important events that affected California in the early 1900s.

Talk About It

COLLABORATE

Look closely at the photo. Who are these people? How do you think these people feel? What details in the photo support your answer?

HSS.4.4.5; HAS.CS.1, HAS.HI.3

McGraw-Hill Education

In 1936, Dorothea Lange took this photo of migrant farm worker Florence Owens Thompson and her children in Nipomo, California.

1 Inspect

Read Look at the title. What do you think this text will be about?

- **Circle** words you don't know.
- **Underline** information that tells you:
  - What is the Dust Bowl?
  - What caused the Dust Bowl?
  - Who was Caroline Henderson?
- **Discuss** with a partner the descriptions of life during the Dust Bowl in Henderson's letter.

My Notes

Huge dust clouds swept over Midwestern farmlands during the Dust Bowl.

Struggles of the Dust Bowl

In the 1930s, a large area of farmland in the middle of the country suffered from an extreme drought, or lack of rainfall. This area became known as the Dust Bowl. The drought lasted about ten years. Without much rain, crops and prairie grasses did not grow. Winds blew across the bare land and picked up dry soil. Huge dust clouds formed. The dust and lack of food and water made life difficult for farmers. Many people in the Dust Bowl had to leave their homes and farms. Many moved to California in search of jobs and new lives.

One person who stayed was Caroline Henderson. She was a farmer in Eva, Oklahoma. Henderson saw many of her neighbors leave. She wrote letters that told about her experiences and struggles as a farmer in the Dust Bowl.

Photo by George E. Marsh, NOAA, Dept. of Commerce

In Their Words ... Caroline Henderson

MY DEAR EVELYN: —

Your continued interest in our effort to 'tie a knot in the end of the rope and hang on' is most stimulating .... Wearing our shade hats, with handkerchiefs tied over our faces and Vaseline in our nostrils, we have been trying to rescue our home from the accumulations of wind-blown dust which penetrates wherever air can go. It is an almost hopeless task, for there is rarely a day when at some time the dust clouds do not roll over ....

Contrary to many published reports, a good many people had left this country either temporarily or permanently .... On a sixty mile trip yesterday to [make tractor] repairs we saw many pitiful reminders of broken hopes and apparently wasted effort. Little abandoned homes where people had drilled deep wells for the precious water, ... and fenced in gardens—with everything now [buried] by banks of drifted soil, told a painful story of loss and disappointment ....

We long for the garden and little chickens, the trees and birds and wild flowers of the years gone by. Perhaps if we do our part these good things may return some day, for others if not for ourselves.

—Caroline Henderson, from a letter written in June 1935

McGraw-Hill Education, TEXT: Henderson, Caroline A. "Letters from the Dust Bowl." *The Atlantic* (May 1936).

2 Find Evidence

Reread What personal experiences do Henderson's letter reveal about the Dust Bowl? What words and phrases tell how she felt about the effects of the Dust Bowl?

Why do you think the abandoned homes told "a painful story of loss and disappointment" for Henderson?

What do the details about the wells and the gardens tell you about her neighbors?

3 Make Connections

Talk Discuss with a partner what life was like for farmers and people during the Dust Bowl.

COLLABORATE

How do the photos on pages 201 and 202 help you understand the effects of the Dust Bowl? What details in Henderson's letter are shown in these photos?

Explore Cause and Effect

Identifying causes and effects can help you understand the connections between events in history. The **cause** is what or why something happened. The **effect** is the result.

1. **Read the text once all the way through.**
   This will help you understand what the text is about.

2. **Identify an important event.**
   What happened? What details describe why the event happened?

3. **Find facts and details that tell the result of what happened.**
   Ask yourself, *Because this happened, what was the result?* The answer is the effect.

COLLABORATE Based on the text you read, work with your class to complete the chart below.

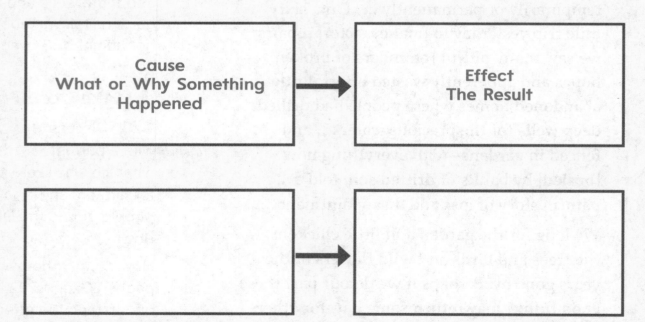

Cause What or Why Something Happened	→	Effect The Result
	→	

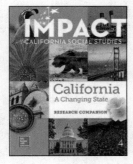

Investigate!

Read pages 240–249 in your Research Companion. Use your investigative skills to identify important events that affected California in the early 1900s. Then look for the causes of the events and the effects. This chart will help you organize your notes.

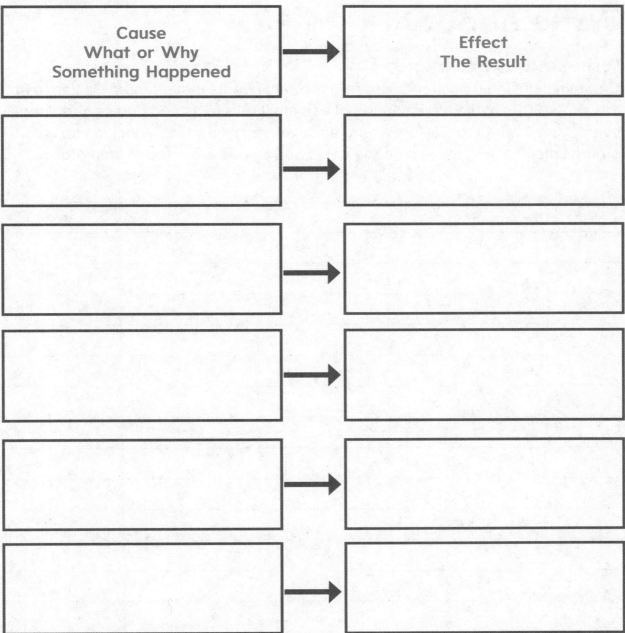

Cause What or Why Something Happened	Effect The Result

Think About It

Evaluate

Review your research. What were the most important events that affected California in the early 1900s? How well did Californians deal with those events?

Write About It

Write and Cite Evidence

Create a time line that shows several important events that affected California in the early 1900s. Write a description of each that tells facts and details about the event, how it affected California, and what caused it to happen. Include images on the time line, and make sure the dates and events are listed in time order.

_____

_____

_____

_____

_____

_____

_____

_____

_____

_____

_____

_____

_____

Talk About It

Compare Your Analysis

Present and discuss your time lines in a small group. How did the information in your time line compare to that in other students' time lines? Discuss which event you think was most important to California and why.

 History

Connect to the

Pull It Together

How did Californians struggle and work together during the early 1900s?

_____

_____

_____

_____

_____

_____

_____

_____

Inquiry Project Notes

_____

_____

_____

_____

_____

How Did California Change After World War II?

Lesson Outcomes

What Am I Learning?

In this lesson, you're going to use your investigative skills to explore how California changed as a result of World War II.

Why Am I Learning It?

Reading and talking about these changes will help you understand the impact of the war on California.

How Will I Know That I Learned It?

You will be able to explain how California's economy, population, and use of resources changed after the war.

Talk About It

Look closely at the photograph. What signs of the bombing can you see? Why do you think the United States entered World War II after this attack?

HSS.4.4.5, HSS.4.4.6

McGraw-Hill Education

On December 7, 1941, the Japanese bombed the U.S. Naval Base at Pearl Harbor in Hawaii.

California

Pearl Harbor, Hawaii

National Archives and Records Administration (NPHS-21-DCHI-IHG-HC298.298REXH14(4)

The Attack at Pearl Harbor

1 Inspect

Read Look at the title. What do you think the primary source—and the text on this page—is about?

- **Circle** words you don't know.
- **Underline** clues that help you answer these questions:
  - What was attacked?
  - Why was the attack important?
  - What were the results of the attack?
- **Discuss** with a partner what Corporal Nightingale saw and heard.

My Notes

_____

_____

_____

_____

_____

_____

_____

_____

_____

On December 7, 1941, Japanese warplanes attacked the U.S. naval base at Pearl Harbor. A naval base provides a place for vessels such as ships and submarines to anchor. It also offers support for the vessels, equipment, and military personnel.

About 2,400 Americans were killed and 1,200 were wounded in the attack. The Pacific Fleet was severely damaged. The naval base lost battleships, destroyers, and aircraft. As a result of the attack, the United States joined the Allied nations to fight the war.

Factories in California produced weapons, ships, and planes to supply the armed forces. Many Californians went to fight the war. New workers stepped up to replace them, including women and African Americans. The Great Depression had caused a shortage of jobs. Now these people could find work in the factories.

When the attack on Pearl Harbor began, Marine Corporal E.C. Nightingale was aboard the *Arizona*, one of the battleships docked there. His words help us understand what happened on that morning.

McGraw-Hill Education, TEXT:Wallin, VADM Homer N. *Pearl Harbor: Why, How, Fleet Salvage and Final Appraisal.* Washington: Naval History Division, 1968.

In Their Words ...
Marine Corporal E.C. Nightingale

"At approximately eight o'clock on the morning of December 7, 1941, I was leaving the breakfast table when the ship's siren for air defense sounded.... Suddenly I heard an explosion. I ran to the port door leading to the quarterdeck and saw a bomb strike a barge of some sort alongside the NEVADA, or in that vicinity. The marine color guard came in at this point saying we were being attacked. I could distinctly hear machine gun fire. I believe at this point our anti-aircraft battery opened up.

"... I started for my battle station .... The men seemed extremely calm and collected. I reached the boat deck and our anti-aircraft guns were in full action, firing very rapidly .... [w]hen it seemed a bomb struck our quarterdeck. I could hear shrapnel or fragments whistling past me ....

"I had only been there a short time when a terrible explosion caused the ship to shake violently. I looked at the boat deck, and everything seemed aflame forward of the mainmast .... [t]he Major ordered us to leave."

—excerpt from *Pearl Harbor: Why, How, Fleet Salvage and Final Appraisal* (1968)

2 Find Evidence

Reread How does Marine Corporal Nightingale's account of the attack help you understand how the attack affected the naval base?

Reread the words, "everything seemed aflame." What do these words mean to you?

3 Make Connections

Talk Discuss with a partner the results of the attack on Pearl Harbor. How did America's joining the war affect the number of jobs in California?

COLLABORATE

How and why did California's workforce change?

Explore Compare and Contrast

Authors often write to **compare** (to show how things are the same or similar) or to **contrast** (to show how things are different).

To compare and contrast:

1. **Read the text once all the way through.**
   This will help you understand what the text is about.

2. **Reread the text. Make sure you understand the most important details.**
   What words or sentences stand out to you as being important?

3. **Look for differences in a topic.**
   For example, how did the types of goods manufactured in California change after the United States went to war?

4. **Look for similarities in a topic.**
   For example, what industries played a part in California's economy both before and after the war?

COLLABORATE Based on what you read, compare and contrast California before and after the attack on Pearl Harbor. How did the war change the state's economy? Work with your class to complete the diagram below.

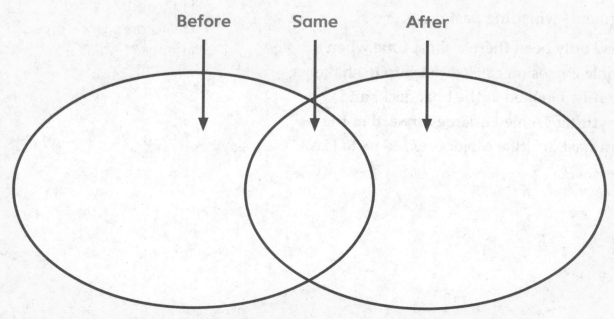

Before   Same   After

Investigate!

Read pages 250–259 in your Research Companion. Use your investigative skills to compare and contrast details about how World War II changed California's economy, population, society, and environment. Use the diagram to organize information.

Before   **Same**   **After**

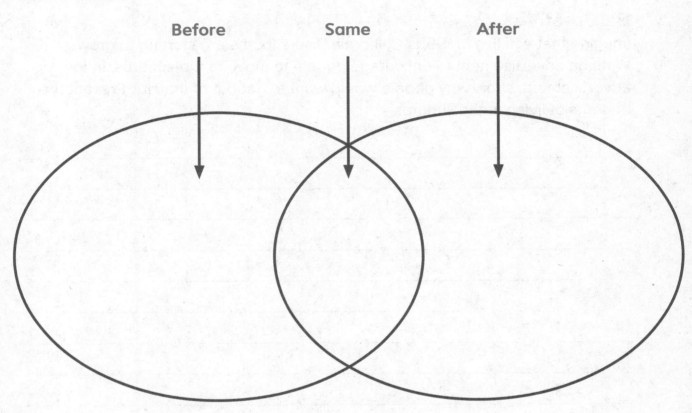

Think About It

Reflect

Review your research. How did World War II change everyday life in California?

Write About It

Be Creative

Imagine that you live in 1950s California. The suburbs are starting to grow. Write an advertisement to encourage people to move to the suburbs. In the advertisement, show why people would want to get out of the city. Present the benefits of living in the suburbs.

_____

_____

_____

_____

_____

_____

_____

_____

_____

_____

_____

_____

_____

_____

_____

_____

Talk About It

Give a Presentation

Present your advertisement to a group of classmates. Have them give their thoughts about your advertisement and the way you presented it.

History

Connect to the

Pull It Together

Think about the people and events that you read and talked about in this lesson. How did California change after World War II?

_____

_____

_____

_____

_____

_____

_____

_____

Inquiry Project Notes

_____

_____

_____

_____

Who Worked for Change in California?

Lesson Outcomes

What Am I Learning?

In this lesson, you're going to use your investigative skills to explore education and the people who worked for change in California.

Why Am I Learning It?

Reading and talking about education and the people who worked for change will help you learn more about why working for change is important.

How Will I Know That I Learned It?

You will be able to explain what it takes to fight for change and the difficulties people face when they want to make a difference.

Talk About It

COLLABORATE

Look at the picture. What words are on the signs the people are holding? What are these people protesting?

HAS.HR.2, HAS.HI.1

Many Californians have worked for change.

Prints and Photographs Division, Library of Congress, LC-DIG-ppmsc-01269, TEXT:(t) Swett, John. *History of the Public School System of California.* San Francisco: A. L. Bancroft & Co., 1876.; (c) King, Martin Luther, Jr. "Remaining Awake Through a Great Revolution." Speech at the Commencement Address at Oberlin College. Oberlin, Ohio, June 1965. Reprinted by arrangement with The Heirs to the Estate of Martin Luther King Jr., c/o Writers House as agent for the proprietor New York, NY. Copyright 1965 Dr. Martin Luther King Jr; copyright renewed 1991 Coretta Scott King.; (b)Chavez, Cesar. "Regaining the Strength." *An Organizer's Tale: Speeches.* Edited by Ilan Stavans. New York: Penguin Books, 2008.

1 Inspect

Read Study each person's quotation.

- **Circle** words you don't know.
- **Underline** words or phrases that tell you what was important to each person.
- **Discuss** with a partner what problems these people were protesting.

My Notes

_____

_____

_____

_____

_____

_____

_____

_____

_____

_____

_____

_____

_____

Speaking Out

Words can be a powerful tool for change. People who have worked for change accomplished great things in part because they inspired others. These leaders gave a voice to those who did not have one. They convinced others to join them. Their words helped change the world. These leaders took chances and showed courage because they believed in a better world where everyone was treated equally and fairly.

PRIMARY SOURCE

In Their Words ...

"If one State in the Union needs a system of free schools more than any other, that State is California. Her population is drawn from all nations."
—John Swett

John Swett

"... the time is always right to do right."
—Martin Luther King, Jr.

"What a terrible irony it is that the very people who harvest the food we eat do not have enough food for their own children."
—Cesar Chavez

Martin Luther King, Jr.

Cesar Chavez

Cesar Chavez was born on an Arizona farm in 1927. His grandparents had come to the United States from Mexico for a better life. In 1938, they lost their land and moved to California. For ten years, they traveled from farm to farm, working long hours for little money.

Cesar Chavez helped farm workers get better wages.

Cesar quit school and worked in the fields. He learned firsthand how bad conditions were for farm workers.

Chavez believed that workers could get better conditions by forming a union. In 1962, Chavez and Dolores Huerta organized the National Farm Workers Association. It later became the United Farm Workers.

Chavez worked tirelessly to improve the lives of farmworkers until the day he died in 1993. Today, Californians celebrate his life and accomplishments every March 31 on the Cesar Chavez Day of Service and Learning.

(bkgd)McGraw-Hill Education; (t)Prints and Photographs Division, Library of Congress Print, LC-DIG-ppmsca-40916

2 Find Evidence

Reread What do you think each quotation means?

Think What makes these quotations effective? How does choice of words reveal emotions?

Reread the quotes and explain how words can inspire positive changes in the world.

3 Make Connections

Talk Take turns reading aloud each quotation with a partner. Discuss the meaning of each quotation.

COLLABORATE

Explore Summary

A **summary** identifies important details and briefly restates them.

1. **Read the text once all the way through.**
   This will help you understand what the text is about.

2. **Look for the main heads and subheads.**
   These heads will help you to see how the text is organized.

3. **Find the people who worked for education and change and what they did.**
   Underline the people's names and the key points about each one.

4. **Restate the important points in your own words.**

 COLLABORATE Based on the text you read, work with your class to complete the chart below.

Name: Cesar Chavez

Detail:	Detail:	Detail:

Summary:

Investigate!

Read pages 260–269 in your Research Companion. Use your investigative skills to identify important details to use to write a summary that tells who worked for education and change. This chart will help you organize your notes.

Name: Olive M. Isbell

Detail:	Detail:	Detail:

Summary:

Name: Martin Luther King, Jr.

Detail:	Detail:	Detail:

Summary:

Name: Harvey Milk

Detail:	Detail:	Detail:

Summary:

Think About It

Connect

Review your research. Based on the information you have gathered,
what personality traits do you think a person needs to have to work for change?

Write About It

Questions

Choose a person who worked for change in California. Think of three questions
you would want to ask that person if you could.

_____

_____

_____

_____

_____

_____

Write and Cite Evidence

Write an interview with the person you chose. Think about the questions you
would want to ask that person and then research how he or she might respond to
those questions.

_____

_____

_____

_____

_____

_____

_____

_____

Talk About It

Role-Play

Take turns reading your interview with a partner. After each reading, discuss the responses to the questions your partner wrote. Do they sound like words the person would have said? Do they reflect that person's personality, beliefs, and actions? Explain your thoughts.

Citizenship

Connect to the

Pull It Together

Who worked for change in California? What were the main contributions these people made?

_____

_____

_____

_____

_____

_____

_____

Inquiry Project Notes

_____

_____

_____

_____

_____

Inquiry Project Wrap Up

The Early 20th Century News Show

Now's the time for your team to present its news segment to the rest of the class. Here's what to do.

☐ Identify for the class the struggle your team will be presenting.

☐ Perform the interviews you have written.

☐ Use visual displays to help develop key ideas.

☐ Provide a final statement that reviews the key ideas presented and explains why the struggle was important in California's history.

Tips for Presenting

Remember these tips when you present to your class.

☐ Rehearse your presentation.

☐ Speak slowly and clearly so that the audience understands what you say.

☐ Look your listeners in the eye.

☐ Practice using video equipment before the presentation.

Project Rubric

Use these questions to help evaluate your project.

	Yes	No
Did our project have a goal?		
Was there a plan that showed what to do and when to do it?		
Did we prepare and perform an interview with a fictional eyewitness of a particular struggle?		
Did our plan work out as expected?		
Did we work well as a team?		

Project Reflection

Think about the work you did to help your team prepare and produce the news show. Describe something that you think you did really well. What would you like to improve next time?

_____

_____

_____

_____

_____

_____

_____

If You Build It, . . .

CHARACTERS

Narrator	Karen	Entire Class
Mr. Roab	Jim	Mary
Mrs. Roab	Teacher	Sam

Narrator: It is 1941 in Salinas, California. We are near a tent in a grove where the Roab family now lives. The Roabs once were farmers in Oklahoma. Then the rains stopped, and a drought set in. Soon the Dust Bowl dried up the land. Without rain, the Roabs could no longer farm. Finally, they were forced to move, and they settled in California. So far, life in California has been hard. Still, the Roabs want their children to go to school and get a good education.

Farm Security Administration/Office of War Information Black-And-White Negatives, Library of Congress, LC-DIG-fsa-8b27115

Narrator: Mrs. Roab calls out to her husband.

Mrs. Roab: It's almost time for lunch!

Karen: Please make lunch for us, too.

Mrs. Roab: Why are you home from school so early?

Karen: It's been a terrible day. The school turned us away.

Jim: They called us "Okies." They said Okies were not welcome in their school.

Mrs. Roab: What are we going to do?

Mr. Roab: I heard about a man named Leo Hart who is starting a school for children of migrants and people like us.

Narrator: That morning, Mr. and Mrs. Roab and their children headed to the new school, but saw that there was no school building. Classes were being taught outside.

Mr. Roab: Pardon me. We're looking for the school that Mr. Hart is opening.

Teacher: This is it.

Entire Class: We still have to build it.

Jim: What do you mean "build it"?

Mary: We're building the school with our bare hands.

Teacher: She's right! We don't have a building yet, but we have acres and acres of land.

Entire Class: Mr. Hart thinks that we'll learn while we're working to build the school.

Teacher: Our students will learn skills like laying bricks, plastering, and painting walls. They will even do some plumbing. We'll build for part of the day and then study the rest of the day.

Mr. Roab: Our kids are good workers, but they've grown a little weak from hunger. It takes a lot of energy to build a school.

Teacher: The school is going to have a working farm. We'll have cows and chickens, and we'll grow our own fruits and vegetables to make our own food.

Mrs. Roab: Well, students, we'd better get started. We have a lot of work left to do!

Narrator: The students went to work. Brick by brick, they built the school.

Mary: I need more bricks.

Jim: How many?

Mary: Let me think. This space takes 6 bricks across and 8 bricks high. Hmmm. 6 × 8 equals 48. I need 48 bricks.

Entire Class: Let's all count out 48 bricks.

Teacher: Kids, it's time for math class.

Narrator: Every day, the students spent time learning to read, write, and do math.

Teacher: You have all done a great job. Mr. Hart had a brilliant idea. What if our school had a science lab?

Entire Class: For science projects?

Teacher: Yes, for research and experiments.

Entire Class: Are we going to build the lab ourselves?

Karen: Look how much we've already accomplished. We can do anything if we put our minds to it!

Teacher: That was exactly what Mr. Hart was hoping you'd say!

Narrator: And so the students began work constructing a science lab.

Karen: I went to the orchard and picked some apples for everyone.

Sam: Thanks. I'm ready for a snack. It's getting hot out here.

Karen: I wish I could dive into a pool and just swim and swim.

Sam: Wouldn't it be great if we had a swimming pool?

Mary: Quit dreaming and get back to work.

Sam: I'm not dreaming. If we can build all of this, why couldn't we build a swimming pool, too?

Entire Class: Let's ask Mr. Hart!

Narrator: Over time, the students built a school, a lab, and a swimming pool. Soon their school became national news. People said it was the best school around. It was all thanks to one man named Leo Hart, who inspired others to make a difference.

Write About It

If you could build your own school, what would you include? Describe everything you would build and tell why you would do it that way.

Chapter

7

California in the
Modern Era

ESSENTIAL **EQ** QUESTION

How Has California Become an Economic and Cultural Leader Since the 1950s?

In this chapter you'll explore how California became a global leader in business, industry, and agriculture. You'll also learn about how the state became a center for movie-making, television, music, literature, and photography.

Talk About It COLLABORATE

Discuss with a partner questions you have about how California became an economic and cultural leader. As you research, look for answers to your questions. Let's get started!

My Research Questions

1. _____

_____

2. _____

_____

3. _____

_____

Inquiry Project

Meet Me at the California State Fair!

In this project, you'll work with a team to plan a visual display that will introduce one of the industries that made California a global economic and cultural leader. Each team will create and present a visual display about the industry of their choice. Your teacher may want to showcase all the displays in one space and invite other classes to attend your California State Fair.

Here's your project checklist.

☐ **Collaborate** with a partner or small group to pick a California industry to research. Make a list of questions to guide your research.

☐ **Research** the industry and its history of innovation. Discover how the industry evolved into a global leader since the 1950s. Each team member should have a specific assignment to research.

☐ **Discuss** your findings with your team.

☐ **Plan** your visual display and how you want to present it. Decide what information to include and how to organize it in a clear way.

☐ **Assemble** your visual display.

☐ **Make** posters to advertise the fair and display them at your school if you plan to invite other classes to visit the fair.

Explore Words

Complete this chapter's Word Rater.
Write notes as you learn more about each word.

aerospace   My Notes
- ☐ Know It!   _____
- ☐ Heard It!   _____
- ☐ Don't Know It!   _____

alternative energy   My Notes
- ☐ Know It!   _____
- ☐ Heard It!   _____
- ☐ Don't Know It!   _____

crisis   My Notes
- ☐ Know It!   _____
- ☐ Heard It!   _____
- ☐ Don't Know It!   _____

entertainment industry   My Notes
- ☐ Know It!   _____
- ☐ Heard It!   _____
- ☐ Don't Know It!   _____

entrepreneur   My Notes
- ☐ Know It!   _____
- ☐ Heard It!   _____
- ☐ Don't Know It!   _____

innovator

- [ ] Know It!
- [ ] Heard It!
- [ ] Don't Know It!

My Notes

_____

_____

_____

microchip

- [ ] Know It!
- [ ] Heard It!
- [ ] Don't Know It!

My Notes

_____

_____

_____

petroleum

- [ ] Know It!
- [ ] Heard It!
- [ ] Don't Know It!

My Notes

_____

_____

_____

service industry

- [ ] Know It!
- [ ] Heard It!
- [ ] Don't Know It!

My Notes

_____

_____

_____

visual arts

- [ ] Know It!
- [ ] Heard It!
- [ ] Don't Know It!

My Notes

_____

_____

_____

Lesson 1

How Have Californian Innovations Changed the World?

Lesson Outcomes

What Am I Learning?

In this lesson, you're going to use your investigative skills to learn how Californian innovations have changed the world.

Why Am I Learning It?

Reading and talking about the new industries from the twentieth and twenty-first centuries will help you understand the role of innovation in California's economy.

How Will I Know That I Learned It?

You will be able to identify innovators from California and explain the global influence of trade on California's economy.

Talk About It

Inspect Look at the picture. What is it? What part of the California economy do you think it represents?

HSS.4.4.6; HAS.CS.2, HAS.CS.5

McGraw-Hill Education

Built under a NASA contract, the GOES (Geostationary Operational Environmental Satellite) system marked a new era in U.S. weather forecasting. Several satellites like this monitor the weather 24 hours a day. They measure weather events in real time.

1 Inspect

Look Study the graph. How do you think it will relate to the text?

- **Highlight** the title.
- **Underline** the years the graph explains.
- **Circle** the points on the graph.
- **Discuss** where the points are heading—up or down.

My Notes

_____

_____

_____

_____

_____

_____

_____

_____

_____

_____

_____

_____

_____

_____

_____

California Exports

California has one of the largest economies in the world. An important part of its economy is international trade. California exports billions of dollars of goods and services all over the world each year.

California exports hundreds of different products. Computers and technology top the list of manufactured goods. The transportation field is second. This includes cars and airplanes. California also ships machinery and exports oil, wine, and a variety of other goods and food products.

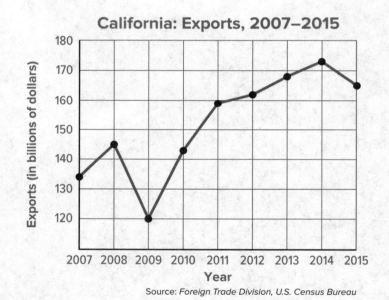

California: Exports, 2007–2015

Source: *Foreign Trade Division, U.S. Census Bureau*

Mexico and Canada are California's top trading partners. Trade with U.S. neighbors is strong because of the North American Free Trade Agreement (NAFTA) of 1992. The three countries agreed not to charge extra fees or limit trade with each other. However, some fear that cheaper imports from Canada and Mexico will put U.S. companies out of business.

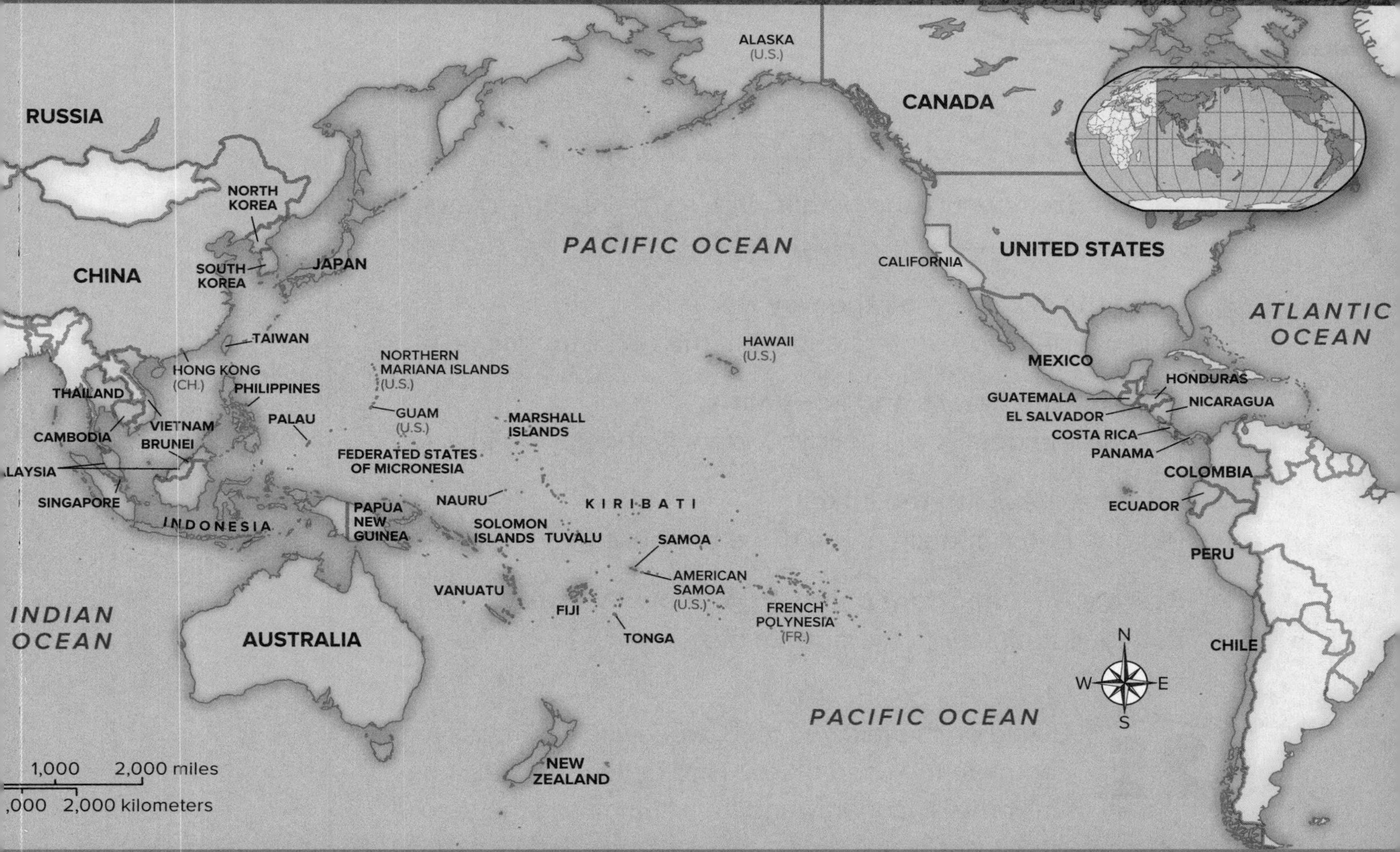

The Pacific Basin

The map shows the Pacific Basin region with the following labels:

RUSSIA · NORTH KOREA · CHINA · SOUTH KOREA · JAPAN · TAIWAN · HONG KONG (CH.) · THAILAND · PHILIPPINES · CAMBODIA · VIETNAM · PALAU · BRUNEI · LAYSIA · SINGAPORE · INDONESIA · PAPUA NEW GUINEA · NORTHERN MARIANA ISLANDS (U.S.) · GUAM (U.S.) · MARSHALL ISLANDS · FEDERATED STATES OF MICRONESIA · NAURU · KIRIBATI · SOLOMON ISLANDS · TUVALU · SAMOA · AMERICAN SAMOA (U.S.) · VANUATU · FIJI · TONGA · FRENCH POLYNESIA (FR.) · NEW ZEALAND · AUSTRALIA

ALASKA (U.S.) · CANADA · UNITED STATES · CALIFORNIA · HAWAII (U.S.) · MEXICO · GUATEMALA · EL SALVADOR · HONDURAS · NICARAGUA · COSTA RICA · PANAMA · COLOMBIA · ECUADOR · PERU · CHILE

PACIFIC OCEAN · INDIAN OCEAN · ATLANTIC OCEAN

1,000 2,000 miles
,000 2,000 kilometers

California also exports a lot of goods and services to other countries around the Pacific Basin. Look at the map to find some top trading partners such as China and Hong Kong, Japan, South Korea, and Taiwan.

2 Find Evidence

Look again In which years did California's exports increase? In which years did they decrease?

Write What problems do you think a trade agreement could cause and why?

3 Make Connections

Think How is California's location on the Pacific Basin important to its economy? How might the advantages of this location change over time?

Explore Summarizing

To **summarize**, identify the details and key points; then retell them briefly in your own words.

1. **Read the text once all the way through.**
   This will help you understand what the text is about.

2. **Look for the details and key points.**
   Finding the details will help you identify the key points.

3. **Add the details to the boxes.**
   Put one detail in each of the three top boxes.

4. **Restate the important points in your own words.**
   Put your summary in the bottom box.

 COLLABORATE Based on the text you read, work with your class to complete the chart below. Find details that describe California's economy and then summarize the details.

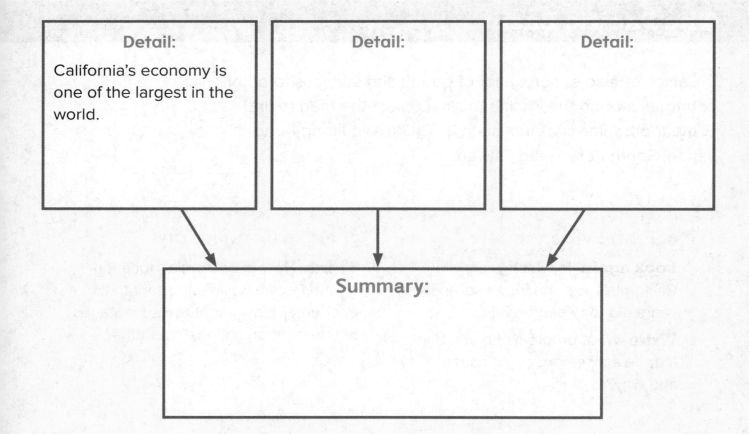

Detail:	Detail:	Detail:
California's economy is one of the largest in the world.		

Summary:

Investigate!

Read pages 280–289 in your Research Companion. Use your investigative skills to identify details about innovations that impacted California's economy. Then write a summary of the details.

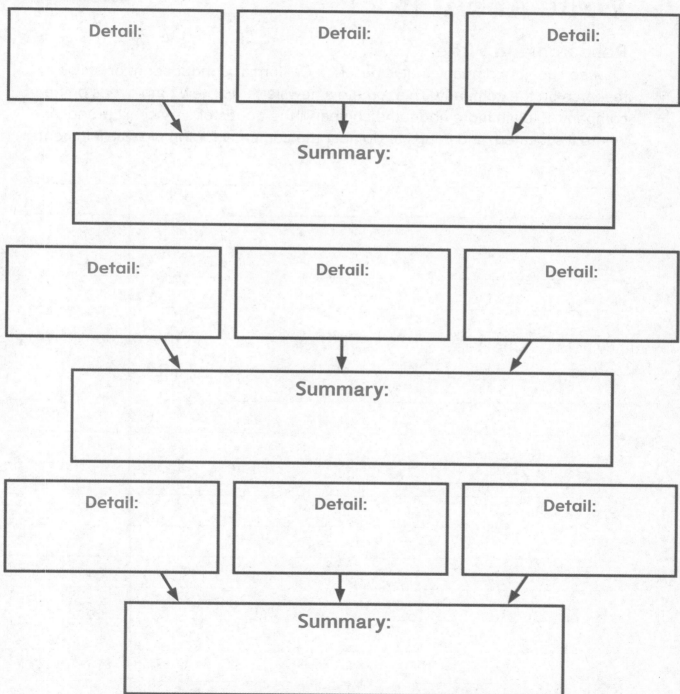

Detail:	Detail:	Detail:

Summary:

Detail:	Detail:	Detail:

Summary:

Detail:	Detail:	Detail:

Summary:

Think About It

Form an Opinion

Review your research. Based on the information you have gathered, which part of the California economy would you want to work in and why?

Write About It

Research and Write

Choose a major company that is based in California. Conduct print or online research on the company. Then create a newsletter for new employees of the company. Explain more about the company, the goods or services it produces, where it's located, and things to do near the company for fun or entertainment.

_____

_____

_____

_____

_____

_____

_____

_____

_____

_____

_____

_____

_____

_____

_____

Talk About It

Compare and Contrast

Exchange newsletters with a partner who chose a different company. Compare and contrast your newsletters. Give each other constructive feedback. Consider changes to your newsletter and revise it based on your partner's input.

Economics

Connect to the

Pull It Together

Think about what you have read and talked about in this lesson. How have California's innovative companies helped the state become an economic and cultural leader? List three ideas to share with others.

_____

_____

_____

_____

_____

_____

Inquiry Project Notes

_____

_____

_____

_____

_____

Lesson 2

How Has California Inspired the Arts?

Lesson Outcomes

What Am I Learning?

In this lesson, you're going to use your investigative skills to explore ways California has inspired the arts.

Why Am I Learning It?

The arts are important in society. Reading and talking about the arts in California will help you understand how California has come to inspire and lead others in the arts.

How Will I Know That I Learned It?

You will be able to identify different forms of art and entertainment developed in California, along with events that inspired them and the people who produced them. You will be able to explain different ways the people of California and the world benefit from the arts.

Talk About It

COLLABORATE

Inspect Look closely at the picture. How would you describe the landscape? What else do you see? How do you know the picture was taken a long time ago? Does anything seem out of place? Explain.

McGraw-Hill Education

In 1923, Hollywood was called "Hollywoodland." The sign was changed to "Hollywood" in 1949.

Analyze the Source

1 Inspect

Read Look at the title. What do you think this text will be about?

- **Circle** words you don't know.
- **Underline** clues that help you answer this question: *What has been the role of entertainment in the arts?*
- **Discuss** with a partner why you think the arts are important.

My Notes

_____

_____

_____

_____

_____

_____

_____

_____

_____

_____

_____

_____

The Arts in California

The arts—literature, music, painting, photography, dance, and film—are important in society. They hold our attention in an enjoyable way with their beauty and creativity. However, the arts are not just entertainment. Their entertainment value is one reason they make a difference in our lives.

The arts are also an important form of communication between people. They help people to become friends, to think about what matters, and to get along with each other. They help people of different cultures and backgrounds understand one another better. The arts bring joy to people's lives.

Ballerina Miko Fogarty studied her art in California and performs internationally.

REUTERS/Alamy Stock Photo

Louis B. Mayer, cofounder of Metro-Goldwyn-Mayer (MGM) Film Studios

2 Find Evidence

Reread How has California's contribution to the arts been unique? Why do you think the entertainment value of the arts brings people around the world together?

3 Make Connections

Talk Discuss with a partner why California has been a leader in bringing the arts to a wide range of audiences.

COLLABORATE

Talk about some reasons why people enjoy entertainment.

California is famous as one of the world's most important centers of arts and entertainment, especially movies and television. As movie makers like Jewish Russian immigrant Louis B. Mayer might have noticed, entertainment has no state or national boundaries. People come from all over the world to share their talent and ideas by working in California's movie and TV studios. Likewise, movies and television have gained large audiences, not only in the United States, but worldwide. California brings the arts to more people than has been possible at any other time in history.

Inquiry Tools

Explore Main Idea and Details

When you identify the **main ideas** and **details** of a text, you find the overall message or purpose of each section and the smaller ideas and specific information that support it. To identify the **main ideas** and **details** of a text:

1. **Read the text once all the way through.**
   This will help you understand what the text is about.

2. **Reread each section and decide what the most important idea is.**
   Often the section titles will help you identify the main idea. Circle the word or words that state this idea.

3. **Look for clues that support this idea.**
   Is there a quote or an image that supports what you're reading about? Are there any words that are repeated that help you understand the main idea?

4. **Look for details that support the main idea.**
   Ask yourself which sentences connect to the main idea. Underline them.

 COLLABORATE

Based on the text you read, work with your class to complete the chart below.

Main Idea	Details
California brings the arts and entertainment to more people than ever around the world.	

Investigate!

Read pages 290–297 in your Research Companion. Use your investigative skills to identify text evidence that tells you the main idea and supporting details of each section. Use the chart to organize information.

Main Idea	Details

Main Idea	Details

Main Idea	Details

Think About It

State an Opinion

Review your research. Based on the information you have gathered, what do you think inspires an artist to create?

Write About It

Create a Work of Art

Think about what you have learned about the many struggles the people of California have faced. Choose one of those struggles and create a work of art to communicate your thoughts and feelings about that struggle. Your artwork can be a story, song, painting, poster, or another form of art. If you create a visual artwork, write a brief explanation or caption to go with it.

_____

_____

_____

_____

_____

_____

_____

_____

_____

_____

_____

_____

_____

_____

_____

Talk About It

Make a Presentation

Present your work of art to the class. Introduce your artwork by telling what you chose as your topic. Then explain briefly the kind of art you created—for example, a story, drawing, or song—and what you wanted to express in your work.

Economics

Connect to the

Pull It Together

Think about the ideas and events that you read and talked about in this lesson. How have the arts and artists helped California's role as an economic and cultural leader?

_____

_____

_____

_____

_____

_____

_____

_____

Inquiry Project Notes

_____

_____

_____

_____

_____

How Is the Environment Important to California's Economy?

Lesson Outcomes

What Am I Learning?

In this lesson, you're going to use your investigative skills to explore the ways in which California's environment has shaped the state's economy.

Why Am I Learning It?

Reading and talking about these issues will help you understand the importance of the environment in how Californians live and use the land.

How Will I Know That I Learned It?

You will be able to explain how agriculture, tourism, and energy use have changed since the 1950s and how California's environment has shaped these industries.

Talk About It

Look closely at the picture. What do you think makes the Central Valley a valuable resource for California? What resources do you see in the picture?

HSS.4.1.5, HSS.4.4.6, HSS.4.4.7; HAS.HI.2

McGraw-Hill Education

Most of California's farmland is in the fertile Central Valley.

1 Inspect

Read Look at the title. What does it suggest about the topic?

- **Circle** words you don't know.
- **Underline** words, phrases, or sentences that help you understand the importance of water to California.
- **Discuss** with a partner the ways in which water is used in the state.
- **Look** at the map. Use your finger to trace one of the Central Valley Project irrigation lines. Where does it start and end? How many miles long is the line?

My Notes

_____

_____

_____

_____

_____

_____

_____

_____

California's Quest for Water

California is the nation's leader in agriculture. The story of California's success in agriculture begins with water. Many crops thrive in California's Central Valley due to its geographic location. The valley lies between the Pacific Coast mountain range and the Sierra Nevada mountain range. This valley has rich soil and many rivers. However, keeping up with the area's demand for water has been a challenge.

Most of California's water comes from the mountains in the northern part of the state. Plenty of rain falls in the northern Sierra Nevada. However, Southern California gets little rain. This area needs a lot of water for people, animals, and crops. In the early 1900s, farmers came up with a solution. They used irrigation, building waterways to carry the water to where it was needed. Since then, farmers in Southern California have depended upon irrigation to help crops grow.

The Shasta Dam was built to collect water for farming. It also supplies electricity to the surrounding area in the form of hydroelectric power.

Geri Lavrov/Stockbyte/Getty Images

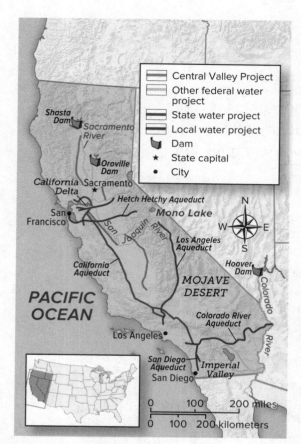

Central Valley Project
Other federal water project
State water project
Local water project
Dam
State capital
City

Shasta Dam
Sacramento River
Oroville Dam
California Delta
Sacramento
Hetch Hetchy Aqueduct
San Francisco
Mono Lake
San Joaquin River
Los Angeles Aqueduct
California Aqueduct
Hoover Dam
MOJAVE DESERT
PACIFIC OCEAN
Colorado River Aqueduct
Colorado River
Los Angeles
San Diego Aqueduct
San Diego
Imperial Valley

N W E S

0   100   200 miles
0   100   200 kilometers

California's water projects supply water to meet the needs of farms and cities.

Bringing water to dry areas was a success. Farmers were able to grow many kinds of crops, such as almonds, apricots, dates, and figs, in the rich soil. The greater water supply also helped cities to support growing numbers of residents.

Since the 1930s, California has created a vast water system to irrigate farmland and to bring water and power to growing cities. The system includes dams, pipelines, canals, and pumping plants. Planning the California State Water Project began in the 1950s. It is California's largest water management project, moving billions of gallons of water across the state.

2 Find Evidence

Reread How do you think California's water projects helped the state become a leader in agriculture? What were other benefits of the water projects?

Look again Look at the map again. How does the map help you visualize the extent of California's water projects?

3 Make Connections

Talk What role has irrigation played in improving California's agriculture?

COLLABORATE

Discuss with a partner the different ways that water is collected for farming.

McGraw-Hill Education

Explore Details that Lead to Conclusions

The **details** in a text and what you already know help you come to a conclusion. A **conclusion** is a decision or judgment. Sometimes a conclusion is an important idea, fact, or answer to a question.

To find the details that lead to a conclusion:

1. **Read the text all the way through to get an overall understanding.**

2. **Identify the author's important details or ideas.**

3. **Look for ways that the important details are related.**
    Ask yourself, *Why is the author telling me this? What is the point?*

4. **Think about what you already know about the topic.**

5. **Put all the details and your prior knowledge together.**
    Ask yourself, *What conclusion, or important point, does this information lead up to?*

 COLLABORATE What role does water play in California's agriculture? Based on the text you read, work with your class to complete the diagram below.

Details
1. Farmers rely on irrigation to grow apricots, figs, and other crops in California.
2.

↓

Conclusion

Investigate!

Read pages 298–307 in your Research Companion. Use your investigative skills to identify details that support the conclusion that California's environment is important to its economy. Use the chart to organize information.

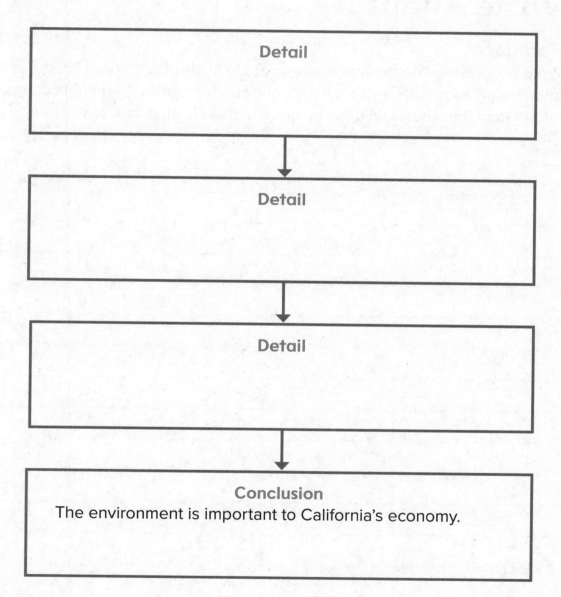

Detail

↓

Detail

↓

Detail

↓

Conclusion
The environment is important to California's economy.

Think About It

Draw Conclusions

Review your research. How do California's climate and geography affect how people use the land?

Write About It

Persuade

Write a tourism guide that persuades people to visit California. Include information about the state's climate, geographic features, and agriculture. Give information that shows why the environment is so important to California.

_____

_____

_____

_____

_____

_____

_____

_____

_____

_____

_____

_____

_____

_____

_____

_____

_____

_____

Talk About It

Compare

Share your tourism guide with a classmate. Compare and contrast the information you included in your tourism guides. Discuss which information best persuades the reader to visit California and why.

Economics

Connect to the

Pull It Together

How has the environment been important in making California an economic leader?

_____

_____

_____

_____

_____

_____

_____

Inquiry Project Notes

_____

_____

_____

_____

_____

_____

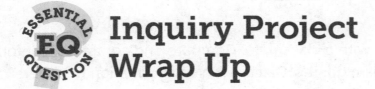

Inquiry Project Wrap Up

Meet Me at the California State Fair!

Now's the time for you and your team to share your visual display. Here's what to do.

Use the display you created to explain how your industry contributed to California's place as an economic and cultural leader.

☐ Present your visual display to the class, using relevant facts and accurate, descriptive details.

☐ Explain why you think your industry has done so well in California.

☐ Answer questions from others about points you made.

Tips for Presenting

Remember these tips when you present to your class.

☐ Prepare your visual display carefully.

☐ Practice what you will say and do to express your ideas.

☐ Speak slowly and clearly so that listeners understand what you say.

☐ Share your enthusiasm for the project.

Project Rubric

Use these questions to help evaluate your project.

	Yes	No
Did we choose one California industry to focus on?		
Did we clearly explain how the industry contributed to California becoming a global leader?		
Did we create an attractive and easy-to-understand visual display?		
Did we use words from the chapter vocabulary?		
Did we work well as a team?		

Project Reflection

Think about the work that you did for this project, either with a group, with a partner, or on your own. Describe what you think you did very well. What have you learned from doing this project?

_____

_____

_____

_____

_____

_____

_____

Chapter 8

The People and Structures That Make California Work

ESSENTIAL **EQ** QUESTION

How Do California's People and Government Help the State Thrive?

In this chapter, you'll explore different levels of California's government. You'll also read about bills and the passing of laws.

Talk About It

COLLABORATE

Discuss with a partner questions you have about the way California's people and structures work within the government. As you research, look for answers to your questions. Let's get started!

My Research Questions

1. _____

_____

2. _____

_____

3. _____

_____

Inquiry Project

Creating a California State Government

In this project, you'll create a California state government in your classroom. This will help you explore how people and structures help California thrive.

Here's your project checklist.

☐ **Recall** what you've learned about California's government. Identify government positions, branches, and their functions.

☐ **Decide** how your class will fill positions in the government you'll be creating. For example, will you draw position titles out of a box? Or will you vote on some positions and have your elected officials appoint others?

☐ **Join** one of the government branches, judicial, legislative, or executive, based on your position.

☐ **Discuss** with the other two groups how a bill would benefit the people if it became law. Talk about the pros and cons. Then work with your group, using judicial, legislative, or executive powers to make the bill become law.

☐ **Agree** on the final wording of the law. Perhaps compare it with an existing California law.

☐ **Present** your new law and discuss how you worked together to develop and approve it.

Explore Words

Complete this chapter's Word Rater.
Write notes as you learn more about each word.

abolish
☐ Know It!
☐ Heard It!
☐ Don't Know It!

My Notes
_____
_____
_____

civil disobedience
☐ Know It!
☐ Heard It!
☐ Don't Know It!

My Notes
_____
_____
_____

democracy
☐ Know It!
☐ Heard It!
☐ Don't Know It!

My Notes
_____
_____
_____

executive branch
☐ Know It!
☐ Heard It!
☐ Don't Know It!

My Notes
_____
_____
_____

judicial branch
☐ Know It!
☐ Heard It!
☐ Don't Know It!

My Notes
_____
_____
_____

legislative branch

☐ Know It!

☐ Heard It!

☐ Don't Know It!

My Notes

_____

_____

_____

multicultural

☐ Know It!

☐ Heard It!

☐ Don't Know It!

My Notes

_____

_____

_____

proposition

☐ Know It!

☐ Heard It!

☐ Don't Know It!

My Notes

_____

_____

_____

refugee

☐ Know It!

☐ Heard It!

☐ Don't Know It!

My Notes

_____

_____

_____

veto

☐ Know It!

☐ Heard It!

☐ Don't Know It!

My Notes

_____

_____

_____

What Powers Belong to the State, Local, and Federal Governments?

Lesson Outcomes

What Am I Learning?

In this lesson, you're going to use your investigative skills to explore the powers that belong to the federal, state, and local governments.

Why Am I Learning It?

Reading and talking about the levels of government will help you learn how federal, state, and local governments work together to serve the people of California and the nation.

How Will I Know That I Learned It?

You will be able to explain the purpose of the United States Constitution and the powers held by federal, state, and local governments.

Talk About It

Look closely at the picture. Who are these people? What do you think they are doing? How do you know?

HSS.4.5.1, HSS.4.5.3

Scene at the Signing of the Constitution of the United States, an oil painting by Howard Chandler Christy, hangs in the United States Capitol.

1 Inspect

Read Look at the title. What do you think this text will be about?

Circle words you don't know.

Underline clues that answer these questions:

- Who attended the Constitutional Convention?
- What happened at the Constitutional Convention?
- How was the United States Constitution made into law?

My Notes

_____

_____

_____

_____

_____

_____

_____

_____

_____

_____

_____

_____

Creating the Constitution

In 1787, the United States was still a new country. It had declared its independence from Great Britain just eleven years earlier. The young nation faced dangers from foreign countries and challenges within its states. Leaders had to decide what role the national government should have in solving the country's problems. So on May 14, 1787, state leaders met in Philadelphia, Pennsylvania, to decide how the country should be governed.

This meeting was called the Constitutional Convention. It lasted from May 14 to September 17. The delegates discussed important questions facing the nation. What powers should the national government have? How should the government be organized to best serve the people?

The delegates had heated debates. On July 24, a few delegates were chosen to write a document that would outline the powers and structure of the national government. This document became the first draft of the United States Constitution.

PRIMARY SOURCE

In Their Words ... John Dickinson

"Let our government be like that of the solar system. Let the general government be like the sun and the states the planets, repelled yet attracted, and the whole moving regularly and harmoniously in several orbits."

—John Dickinson, Delaware Delegate, 1787

TEXT: Dickinson, John. Speaking before the Constitutional Convention, June 4, 1787.

The United States Constitution became the law of the nation in 1788.

When the draft was finished, all of the delegates discussed the new Constitution. They reviewed every word and made many changes. On September 17, 1787, most of the delegates approved the document. It was then sent to the states.

In order for Constitution to become law, nine of the thirteen states had to approve it. For many months, people throughout the country argued for and against the draft of the Constitution. Some people supported it. Others believed that it gave too much power to the national government. They wanted to make sure that the U.S. Constitution did not define state or local government powers.

Over time, more and more states voted in support of the Constitution. Finally, on June 21, 1788, New Hampshire became the ninth state to officially approve the Constitution. From that day forward, the Constitution became the law of the nation.

2 Find Evidence

Reread Why was there disagreement on the power that the national government should have? What details did the author include about people's opinions?

How does the quotation by John Dickinson relate to the information in the text? What words and phrases does Dickinson use to describe how the government should be like the solar system?

3 Make Connections

Talk Discuss with a partner why the Constitution was an important document for the United States. What details in the text support your answer?

COLLABORATE

Inquiry Tools

Explore Compare and Contrast

When you **compare and contrast**, you explain how two or more things are alike and different. Comparing and contrasting helps you identify similarities and differences among events and ideas.

1. **Read the text once all the way through.**
   This will help you understand what the text is about.

2. **Look for key facts and details that show differences about similar topics.**
   How are the topics different? Which facts and details show these differences?

3. **Look for key facts and details that show similarities about the topics.**
   How are the topics the same? Which facts and details show these similarities?

4. **Use key facts or details to compare and contrast the topics.**
   Use important facts and details to explain how the topics are alike and how they are different.

COLLABORATE Based on the text you read, work with your class to complete the chart below.

Powers of Each Level of Government		
Federal Government	**State Government**	**Local Government**

Investigate!

Read pages 318–325 in your Research Companion. Use your investigative skills to identify the similarities and differences among federal, state, and local governments. Use the chart to organize information.

Powers of Each Level of Government		
Federal Government	**State Government**	**Local Government**

Think About It

Sum Up

Review your research. Based on the information you have gathered, how do federal, state, and local governments share power and responsibilities?

Talk About It

COLLABORATE

Take a Stand

With a partner, discuss how the Constitution outlines the powers of the federal government and state government. If you were a founding father, would you have wanted federal and state powers to be divided this way? Identify and discuss the reasons and evidence your partner gives to support his or her position.

_____

_____

_____

_____

_____

_____

_____

_____

_____

_____

_____

_____

_____

_____

_____

_____

Write About It

Explain

Imagine that you were one of the founding fathers at the Constitutional Convention. Write a letter to your family that explains the purpose of the Constitution and the powers of federal, state, and local governments.

Civics

Connect to the

Pull It Together

Why are federal, state, and local governments each important to the state of California?

_____

_____

_____

_____

_____

Inquiry Project Notes

_____

_____

_____

_____

_____

_____

_____

How Are California's State and Local Governments Organized?

Lesson Outcomes

What Am I Learning?

In this lesson, you're going to use your investigative skills to understand how state and local governments are organized.

Why Am I Learning It?

Reading and talking about state and local governments will help you understand the different responsibilities of each.

How Will I Know That I Learned It?

You will be able to explain the form and function of both state and local governments.

Talk About It

Examine Look closely at the picture. Where are these people? What might the robes symbolize?

HSS.4.5.5

272 Lesson 2 How Are California's State and Local Governments Organized?

Two judges work with a student from the University of California.

1 Inspect

Read Look at the heading and read the article. What questions do you have about tribal governments?

- **Circle** words that you don't know.
- **Underline** clues that help you answer the questions *Who, What, Where, When,* or *Why.*
- **Discuss** with a partner how tribal government works with state government.

My Notes

_____

_____

_____

_____

_____

_____

_____

_____

_____

_____

_____

Tribal Governments

One important type of local government is tribal government. This type of local government works differently from most local governments. Most local governments are smaller parts of the state government. But tribal governments are completely separate from the state government.

Because tribes were present before the settlers, tribes are allowed to govern themselves. In fact, the United States Constitution protects tribal government rights. It is important for tribal people to keep their culture and identities. They are allowed to govern themselves on their reservations and rancherias, which are small Indian settlements.

Tribal governments can create their own government structure. They do not have to follow state government. This means that tribes can create their own laws and enforce their laws through their tribal courts. Just like state and local governments, tribal governments provide programs and services to their people. These include education, energy, roads, bridges, and public buildings.

Tribal governments are separate from the state, but they need to work with the state at times. Tribal people need access to federal programs that are allowed to all citizens. This might be handled at the state level. Tribes may also need to work with the state on environmental issues that affect tribal land.

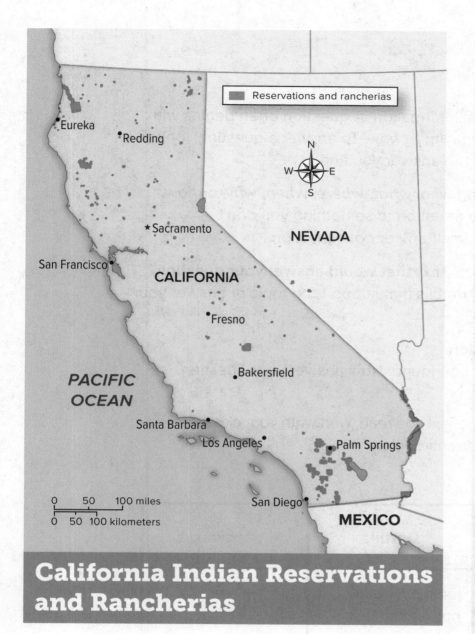

Reservations and rancherias

Eureka
Redding
N
W E
S
Sacramento
NEVADA
San Francisco
CALIFORNIA
Fresno
PACIFIC OCEAN
Bakersfield
Santa Barbara
Los Angeles
Palm Springs
0 50 100 miles
0 50 100 kilometers
San Diego
MEXICO

California Indian Reservations and Rancherias

2 Find Evidence

Reread What does the text suggest about how tribal governments differ from other local governments? What details support your answer?

Reread In what ways do tribal governments have to work with the state government? Give two details from the text that support your answer.

3 Make Connections

Talk What kinds of services do the tribal governments provide for their communities?

COLLABORATE

Talk about the reasons why these services would be important.

Explore Ask and Answer Questions

We ask questions to get information. A question often begins with *who, what, where, when why,* or *how.* To answer a question, look for details that support the answer you find.

1. **Ask a question using *who, what, where, when, why,* or *how.***
   When you read, pay attention to something you don't understand. Ask yourself a *W* or *how* question.

2. **Look for details in the text that would answer your question.**
   Look for supporting details that support the topic or answer your question.

3. **Answer your question.**
   Use the details that you found. Now answer your question.

COLLABORATE

Based on the text you read, work with your class to complete the chart below.

Question	Details	Answer
How is tribal government organized?	local but not part of state government; make own laws; provide services to people on reservations, rancherias	

Investigate!

Read pages 326–335 in your Research Companion. Use your investigative skills to identify text evidence that tells you how state and local governments are organized.

Question	Details	Answer
How is state government organized?		
How is local government organized?		

Think About It

Compare
What is the difference between state and local governments?

Write About It

Write a Newspaper Article
Imagine you are a journalist who is describing the organization of state and local governments. Conduct research to identify the leaders that represent your community in state and local governments. Include a list of these leaders at the end of your article.

_____

_____

_____

_____

_____

_____

_____

_____

_____

_____

_____

_____

_____

_____

_____

_____

Talk About It

Share

In a small group, discuss which position in local government interests you most and why. Discuss the powers and responsibilities of each position that is mentioned.

Civics

Connect to the

Pull It Together

How do state and local governments help the citizens of California?

_____

_____

_____

_____

_____

_____

_____

_____

_____

Inquiry Project Notes

_____

_____

_____

_____

Who Are Californians Today and Where Do They Live?

Lesson Outcomes

What Am I Learning?

In this lesson, you will use your investigative skills to gain an understanding of the diversity within California's environment, population, architecture, and transportation.

Why Am I Learning It?

Reading and talking about the diversity within California will help you make inferences about how culture and environment impact the daily life of Californians.

How Will I Know That I Learned It?

You will be able to make inferences about how Californians adapt to their environment and to changing communities.

Talk About It

COLLABORATE

Examine Look at the image. What were the people in the photo doing? How does the photo show diversity?

HSS.4.1.3, HSS.4.1.5

California has a diverse population that includes people from many different backgrounds.

Eric Raptosh/Hill Street Studios/Getty Images

1 Inspect

Read Look at the title. What do the words "New Immigrants" suggest about the topic of this text?

- **Circle** words you don't know.
- **Underline** clues that help you understand the diversity of California's population.
- **Discuss** with a partner the people who live in your community and how they are similar to or different from the people described on these pages.

My Notes

_____

_____

_____

_____

_____

_____

_____

_____

_____

_____

Responding to New Immigrants

California has a history of immigration. Over the years, immigrants have come from different countries at different times. Now many immigrants to California come from Mexico and Central America. As these immigrants enter California, there are social, political, and economic impacts on the community.

New immigrants bring different cultures to the community. They bring new concerns, new strengths, and new leaders. They bring different economic needs and create new economic opportunities. They often bring different sets of skills and work in different industries. Communities react differently to new immigrants. Some welcome new immigrants openly, while others are uncomfortable with change.

The Latino population in California is growing.

Hill Street Studios/Getty Images

In Their Words ... Adam Nagourney and Jennifer Medina

"One lingering issue is voting rules. Although Santa Ana has an all-Latino City Council, there are no Latino Council members in neighboring Anaheim, even though the city is almost half Latino. Anaheim, like several other communities, elects its Council at large, rather than by district, which tends to put Latinos, who turn out smaller numbers than the general electorate, at a disadvantage."

—from "This City Is 78% Latino, and the Face of a New California," *The New York Times*, October 11, 2016

2 Find Evidence

Reread Do you think the author of the text on page 282 believes that immigrants have made positive or negative contributions to the community? How do you know?

Analyze Reread the paragraph from *The New York Times*. What two communities are the reporters comparing? What is the difference they point out? What is the cause of this difference, according to the reporters?

3 Make Connections

Talk What role might California's location play in immigration? Why might people come here?

COLLABORATE

How do you think the diversity of immigrants can benefit a community?

Inquiry Tools

Explore Making Inferences

Making Inferences means using text evidence or clues in the text to draw conclusions that the author might not state directly. Readers can apply what they already know about a topic to the evidence or clues in a text to figure out information that is not stated directly.

1. **Read the text once all the way through.**
   This will help you understand what the text is about.

2. **Look at the clues or evidence that are in the text.**
   What facts, data, or details does the author provide as evidence?

3. **Add knowledge you already have that relates to these clues.**
   What are some things you already know that you can connect to this information?

4. **Think about the connections between your prior knowledge and the clues and evidence in the text.**
   What can you infer, based on the evidence and what you already know?

 COLLABORATE Based on the text you read, work with your class to make inferences about the local government and Latino voters in Anaheim.

Text Clues	What You Know	Inferences
There are no Latino Council members in Anaheim. The city is almost half Latino.		

Investigate!

Read pages 336–343 in your Research Companion. Use your investigative skills to make inferences about how Californians adapt to their environment and to changing communities.

Text Clues	What You Know	Inferences

Think About It

Generalize

Review your research. Based on the information you have gathered, how would you describe the people of California and their communities?

_____

_____

_____

_____

Write About It

Personal Observation

Based upon your experience, write a reflection about the diversity of people you have encountered in California. How does a diverse population affect your community and your day-to-day life?

_____

_____

_____

_____

_____

_____

_____

_____

_____

_____

Talk About It

Share

Share your reflection with other students in a small group. Discuss details and examples that were most vivid and memorable in your classmates' reflections.

Citizenship

Connect to the

Pull It Together

How is the diversity of people and environments important to life in California?

_____

_____

_____

_____

_____

_____

_____

_____

Inquiry Project Notes

_____

_____

_____

_____

_____

What Are the Rights and Responsibilities of Californians?

Lesson Outcomes

What Am I Learning?

In this lesson, you are going to use your investigative skills to explore the rights and responsibilities of Californians.

Why Am I Learning It?

Reading and talking about rights and responsibilities will help you learn more about how California's government works and the role citizens play in it.

How Will I Know That I Learned It?

You will be able to explain the rights and freedoms of Californians and the responsibilities Californians have to make sure the government works for everyone.

Talk About It

Discuss Read the quote. Why does President Roosevelt say that voting is important? What does he mean when he says that the American people are the only ones who can deprive themselves of the right to vote?

HSS.4.5.2

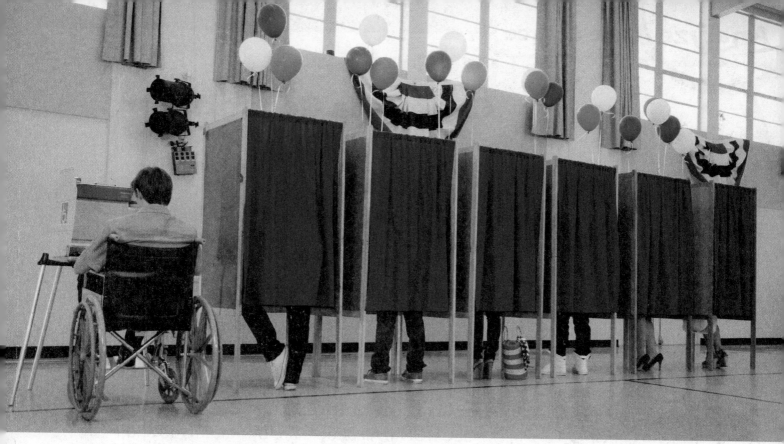

Voting is one way Californians exercise their rights.

Blend Images-Hill Street Studios/Brand X Pictures/Getty Images;
TEXT: President Franklin D. Roosevelt's Radio Address from the White House, October 5, 1944.

PRIMARY SOURCE

In Their Words... Franklin Delano Roosevelt

"Nobody will ever deprive the American people of the right to vote except the American people themselves—and the only way they could do that is by not voting at all.

The continuing health and vigor of our democratic system depends on the public spirit and devotion of its citizens which find expression in the ballot box.

Every man and every woman in this Nation—regardless of party—who have the right to register and to vote, and the opportunity to register and to vote, have also the sacred obligation to register and to vote. For the free and secret ballot is the real keystone of our American Constitutional system."

—President Franklin D. Roosevelt, 1944 Radio Address

1 Inspect

Read Look at the title. What do you think this article will be about?

- **Circle** words you don't know.
- **Underline** key words or phrases that help you understand what each of these sections of the California Constitution is about.
- **Discuss** with a partner each of the rights described in the article.

My Notes

_____

_____

_____

_____

_____

_____

_____

_____

_____

_____

_____

_____

_____

_____

California Constitution

California has had two Constitutions. The first was adopted in 1849 before California was admitted to the United States. The current California Constitution was adopted in 1879. The Constitution is organized into Articles. Each Article is organized into Sections. Article I is the Declaration of Rights. It explains the rights of the people of California. Below are some excerpts from the document.

Article I

Declaration of Rights

SECTION 1. All people are by nature free and independent and have inalienable rights. Among these are enjoying and defending life and liberty, acquiring, possessing, and protecting property, and pursuing and obtaining safety, happiness, and privacy.

SECTION 2. (a) Every person may freely speak, write and publish his or her sentiments on all subjects, being responsible for the abuse of this right. A law may not restrain or abridge liberty of speech or press.

SECTION 4. Free exercise and enjoyment of religion without discrimination or preference are guaranteed....

SECTION 5. The military is subordinate to civil power. A standing army may not be maintained in peacetime. Soldiers may not be quartered in any house in wartime except as prescribed by law, or in peacetime without the owner's consent.

TEXT: Calif. Const. art I, §1, §2a, §4, §5, §8, §20, §29, §31a.

Certain freedoms are guaranteed by the California Constitution, such as the freedom of speech.

SECTION 8. A person may not be disqualified from entering or pursuing a business, profession, vocation, or employment because of sex, race, creed, color, or national or ethnic origin.

SECTION 20. Noncitizens have the same property rights as citizens.

SECTION 29. In a criminal case, the people of the State of California have the right to due process of law and to a speedy and public trial.

SECTION 31. (a) The State shall not discriminate against, or grant preferential treatment to, any individual or group on the basis of race, sex, color, ethnicity, or national origin in the operation of public employment, public education, or public contracting.

2 Find Evidence

Reread What do you think is the purpose of Section 2. (a)?

Reread Section 1. Who are these rights for? What do the words *acquiring, possessing,* and *protecting* mean? Name three words that have almost the same meaning as each of the words.

3 Make Connections

Talk Discuss with a partner the rights given by the California Constitution. What are some ways you have seen people exercise, or use, these rights?

COLLABORATE

Explore Main Idea and Details

The main idea of a text tells what the text is about. The main idea is supported by details. These details provide more specific information about the topic.

To understand main idea and details:

1. **Read the text all the way through.**

2. **Reread the text and try to determine what the text is mostly about, or its main idea.**
   Ask yourself, *What does the author want me to know?*

3. **Read on to identify the details that support the main idea.**
   Look for sentences that give more information or help you understand an idea better.

COLLABORATE Based on the text you read, work with your class to complete the chart below.

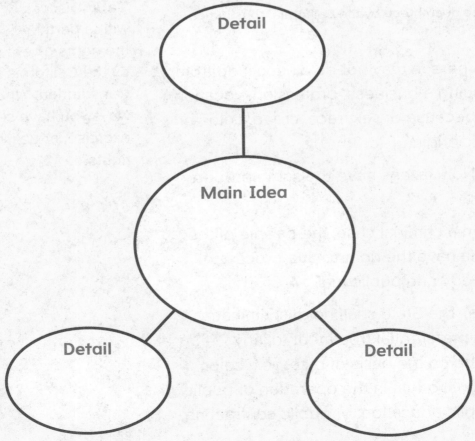

Investigate!

Read pages 344–353 in your Research Companion. Use your investigative skills to identify the main idea and details about the rights and responsibilities of Californians.

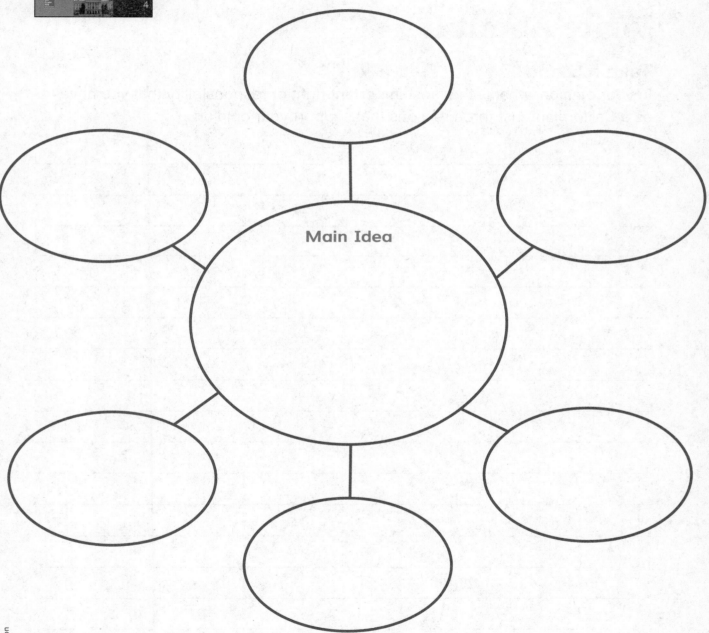

Main Idea

McGraw-Hill Education

Think About It

Summarize

Review your research. Based on the information you have gathered, what rights and responsibilities do Californians have?

Write About It

Take a Stand

In your opinion, what is the most important right or responsibility that you have as a Californian? List three reasons that support your opinion.

_____

_____

_____

_____

_____

_____

_____

_____

_____

_____

_____

_____

_____

_____

_____

_____

_____

Talk About It

COLLABORATE

Evaluate Evidence

Take turns reading your opinions with a partner. Paraphrase your partner's opinion and identify which reasons you think most strongly support his or her opinion.

Civics

Connect to the

ESSENTIAL EQ QUESTION

Pull It Together

Why is it important to understand your rights and responsibilities? How can this help you be a better citizen and help California thrive?

_____

_____

_____

_____

_____

_____

_____

_____

_____

_____

ESSENTIAL EQ QUESTION

Inquiry Project Notes

_____

_____

_____

_____

Inquiry Project Wrap Up

Creating a California State Government

Now's the time for you to discuss your new law as a class. Here's what to do.

☐ Explain how you developed your government.

☐ Discuss the steps you took to form your three branches.

☐ Describe how each branch functions.

☐ Talk about how well you think your government worked. Discuss the pros and cons of working in government based on your experience.

Tips for Presenting

Remember these tips when you present to your class.

☐ Follow the rules your group has agreed on.

☐ Present a logical sequence of ideas, using facts to support the ideas.

☐ Summarize the key points in your written law.

☐ Allow audience members to pose specific questions, and take turns with group members to respond to each question.

Project Rubric

Use these questions to help evaluate your project.

	Yes	No
Did my role reflect an official position within one of the three branches of government?		
Did we identify a clear need for a bill that could become law?		
Acting within our branch of government, did we show respect for the roles of the other two branches of government?		
Did I listen to my classmates' ideas?		
Did I ask and answer questions to help share clear understandings?		
Did our final presentation include a clearly worded law?		

Project Reflection

Think about the work that you did on this project, either with your group or on your own. Describe which part of the project was most helpful to do in a group. Which part was most helpful to do on your own?

_____

_____

_____

An International Day to Remember

CHARACTERS

Narrator	Mr. Lee	Miguel
Ronit	Jana	Ms. Franklin
Chorus	Rick	
Carl	Mei	

Narrator: It was Thursday in Oak Valley School.

Chorus: Oak Valley School? Where's that?

Narrator: It's located in a community in southern California. All over the valley, there are majestic oak trees. Above the valley there are rugged mountains. And beyond the mountains to the west, you can see—

Chorus: The Pacific Ocean!

Narrator: That's right. Over time, this once small town had grown into a city as families moved here from across the United States and around the world.

Chorus: They helped make Oak Valley what it is today.

Narrator: That's right. Well, on one particular Thursday, the weather in Oak Valley was sunny, but the mood in Mr. Lee's fourth grade classroom was gloomy.

Chorus: Oh, no! What happened?

Narrator: Mr. Lee's class was supposed to go on a field trip to the Cultural Center. They were going to take part in an International Day.

Chorus: Sounds interesting! Um, what *is* an International Day?

Narrator: It's a day that celebrates all the cultures that make California such a great place to live.

Chorus: That's wonderful!

Narrator: But they did not go.

Chorus: That's terrible! What happened?

Narrator: The bus broke down and Mr. Lee could not get another bus in time.

Chorus: What happened next?

Narrator: Come see for yourself. This is Mr. Lee's classroom, and here are his students.

Chorus: They sure look disappointed.

Narrator: They do. If only someone had an idea.

Rick: [raises his hand] Mr. Lee?

Mr. Lee: Yes, Rick?

Rick: I have an idea.

Chorus: Yay!

Narrator: Ssh! You don't even know what it is yet.

Rick: Since we can't go to International Day, what if International Day comes to us?

Ronit: Oh, I see! We could hold our own International Day at Oak Valley School!

Mei: Oh, could we, Mr. Lee? After all, we have so many different cultures right here in our own city. We could celebrate with traditional food. I can bring Chinese noodles.

Carl: Good idea! I can ask my parents to help me make some traditional Caribbean dishes.

Jana: Like cornmeal dumplings and fresh papaya.

Ronit: I know how to make *challah* bread from Israel.

Miguel: Well, I make the best Mexican salsa.

Mr. Lee: Wow! Perhaps we could do our own International Day. But can we also come up with some activities? After all, food is just one part of California's cultural traditions.

Mei: What if we share other things that tell about our cultures? Have you ever seen the Dragon Dance at Chinese New Year? When my family and I saw it in San Francisco, I made a video of it.

Rick: Cool! I don't have video, but I could teach people how to do Irish dance. Some of my family play Irish instruments.

Carl: And stories! Our next-door neighbor, Mrs. Somé, is a *griot*. That means she's a storyteller. She grew up hearing stories about West Africa and now she tells stories at our local library. I'm sure she would help us.

Jana: I want to add to Carl's suggestion. Along with stories and folk tales, we could also share true accounts. For example, I could tell about how my mom and dad moved to Oak Valley from Bangalore. It was a big change! My sister and I were born here and we're always pestering them to tell us what it was like to emigrate from India to America.

Mr. Lee: You all have great ideas! Are there any more suggestions you want to add?

(All of Mr. Lee's students raise their hands.)

Narrator: As you can see, the sunny day had turned into a storm—a *brainstorm*! Over the next few weeks, Mr. Lee asked the school principal and the other teachers about holding an International Day. Then he sent a letter home inviting all the families to take part.

Chorus: What did they say?

Narrator: They said yes! Everyone was so excited. The teachers were excited, the parents were excited, and Mr. Lee's students—

Chorus: —were the most excited of all!

Narrator: That's right. Day after day, they came up with more ways to celebrate each other's cultures. They folded Japanese origami and wrote haiku. They made a mural about Ohlone people in early California. They found pictures of handmade crafts from Central America. They even recorded a speech about the contributions of each culture to California.

Chorus: That's amazing!

Narrator: Oh, that was just the beginning. Just listen to this—

Mr. Lee: So remember, many 20th century artists from California made a big impact on the cultural development of the United States. *(Sees that Jana has raised her hand.)* Yes, Jana?

INTERNATIONAL DAY
- CULTURAL TRADITIONS
- FOOD, MUSIC, DANCE
- CULTURES OUR SCHOOL REPRESENTS

Jana: That gives me another idea for our International Day. We could make a display to show that these artists represent many different cultures. I wonder if any of those artists have a connection to Oak Valley?

Carl: We could add the display to the gallery we made. It could be part of our "California Loves Culture" exhibit. Did you know that California is the most culturally diverse state in the United States?

Mei: It's true! I found out some interesting facts as I was researching how to make a population map of California. People from all over the world already call California home, and one out of every four immigrants to the United States chooses to settle here.

Mr. Lee: I can see that you have all done your homework!

Miguel: That's good, because International Day is less than a week away!

Narrator: Finally, the big day came. That morning, Mr. Lee gave his class some final tips.

Mr. Lee: Be sure to greet everyone politely. Make eye contact and remember to smile. Listen carefully, in case someone has a question or does not understand something.

Mr. Lee's Class: Yes, Mr. Lee.

Mr. Lee: Oh, and one more thing. A surprise guest is joining us.

Chorus: A surprise guest? Who could it be?

Narrator: The students wondered, too. Then they opened the doors and invited all the families, neighbors, other students, and teachers to come inside. It was a great day.

Chorus: A great day!

Narrator: There was singing and dancing—

Chorus: Singing and dancing!

Narrator: Good food and games—

Chorus: Good food and games!

Narrator: Everybody learned a lot, and everybody had—

Chorus: —a wonderful time!

Narrator: And then—

Chorus: And then?

Narrator: Mr. Lee introduced a woman named Ms. Franklin. Now Ms. Franklin had been taking photographs all day. But who was she?

Chorus: A mom? A teacher? A neighbor?

Mr. Lee: I would like you all to meet Ms. Franklin. Ms. Franklin is the director of the Cultural Center. I wrote to her about the day we had to cancel our field trip. I told her about our plans.

Ms. Franklin: Hello! When Mr. Lee told me about how you planned an International Day of your own, I wanted to see it for myself. Now that I have, I am so impressed that I have a big announcement to make.

Chorus and Mr. Lee's class: What? What?

Narrator and Mr. Lee: Listen and find out!

Ms. Franklin: The Cultural Center plans to host a special exhibit inspired by— you! Our exhibit will show people how you planned an International Day right in your own community. It will show visitors from all over California how they can do this, too!

Everyone: Hurray!

Narrator: And that's the story of how one group of students turned a challenge into an opportunity. After all, sharing all our ideas is what makes California—

Everyone: A great place to live!

Write About It

If you could have an International Day with your class what would you do? Describe the different kinds of food and activities your class could share.

Reference Sources

The Reference Section has a glossary of vocabulary words from the chapters in this book. Use this section to explore new vocabulary as you investigate and take action.

Glossary

A

abolish To stop or end a practice or a law.

adapt To change to fit a place.

aerospace The science or industry of travel by air or in space.

agriculture The business of farming or raising livestock.

alternative energy Energy produced from a renewable resource that creates little or no pollution.

amendment A change in the words or meaning of a law or document (such as a constitution).

aqueduct A pipe or other channel that carries water over long distances.

artifact An object that humans create to help them accomplish a task.

B

boomtown A town that builds up quickly around an industry or economic opportunity.

boycott A refusal to buy a certain product to bring attention to a problem.

bribe Something of value offered to sway someone in one direction or another.

C

Californio People from Alta California.

campus The property around the buildings of a school, college, or business.

civil disobedience The act of peacefully protesting by refusing to comply with a law or rule.

claim An area of land to which a miner declares exclusive rights to mine for gold.

colony A territory ruled by a distant country.

communication An exchange of information.

compromise A plan in which both sides give up something.

constitution A document outlining the rights and responsibilities of the government.

convert To change the religious beliefs of a person or people from one religion to another.

costs and benefits A way to judge risks and opportunities.

crisis A difficult situation that needs immediate attention.

delegates Representatives of the people.

democracy A form of government that is run by its people.

deport To make someone leave a country.

discrimination The act of treating a person or a group unfairly from other people or groups.

drought A long period of time with little rainfall.

empire A group of lands or countries ruled by one government.

entrepreneur A person who starts a business.

executive branch The part of the government that enforces the laws of a country.

expedition A journey for a particular purpose.

hemispheres One of two equal halves of a sphere, such as the Earth.

immigrant A person who moves from one country to live in another.

inhabitants The people who live in a place.

innovator A person who shows something new.

internment camps *Internment* means putting a person in prison or other kind of detention, generally in wartime. During World War II, the American government sent many Japanese Americans to *internment* camps, fearing that they might be loyal to Japan.

investor Someone who gives money to start a project.

irrigation The use of canals, ditches, and pipes to bring water to dry land.

judicial branch A system of courts that explain the laws of a country.

land grant A gift of land provided by the government.

latitude An imaginary line of distance north or south of the Equator.

legislative branch The government body that writes the laws of a country.

levee A mound of earth built along a river to prevent flooding.

longitude An imaginary line of distance east or west of the Prime Meridian.

Manifest Destiny In American history, the belief that westward expansion could not be stopped or delayed.

manufacture A way of making things with machines instead of by hand.

mestizo A person of mixed race; usually European and American Indian.

microchip A tiny computer part that allows a computer to make calculations.

migrate To move from one place to another.

mission A religious settlement or church.

multicultural Relating to or including many different cultures.

opportunity The chance to improve or grow.

petroleum Oil that is the base of gasoline and other products.

pioneer The first settlers of a new area.

plateau A high, flat area of land that is higher than the land around it.

presidios Fortified military outpost or fort. The Spanish presidios in Alta California included public and military settlements and a chapel.

proposition A plan or offer sent to a government.

public education A system of schools that are funded and run by a local government.

pueblos The non-Indian towns established to help colonize Alta California.

rebel To oppose.

reform Changes in government.

refrigeration The process of making or keeping things cold.

refugee A person who was forced to leave his or her home country because of war, disaster, or persecution.

republic A country that has elected representatives and a head of state.

reservoir A lake used to store water.

revert Return back to what once was.

revolt A fight against authority.

risk To put in danger.

segregation A form of discrimination that keeps different groups of people separate.

service industry A business that gives services to people.

suffrage The right to vote.

trailblazer A guide, a person who prepares a path for others to follow.

transcontinental Going across a continent.

trapper A hunter who uses traps to catch animals for their fur.

treaty An agreement that two or more countries make.

vaquero A cowboy.

veto A decision by a person in authority to not allow or approve something (such as a new law).

visual arts Painting, sculpture, photography, and other artistic works that people must see to understand.

W

World War II The war that was fought by many countries, mainly in Europe and Asia, from 1939 to 1945

Grade Four
Historical and Social Sciences Content Standards and Analysis Skills

History-Social Sciences Content Standards

California: A Changing State

Students learn the story of their home state, unique in American history in terms of its vast and varied geography, its many waves of immigration beginning with pre-Columbian societies, its continuous diversity, economic energy, and rapid growth. In addition to the specific treatment of milestones in California history, students examine the state in the context of the rest of the nation, with an emphasis on the U.S. Constitution and the relationship between state and federal government.

4.1 Students demonstrate an understanding of the physical and human geographic features that define places and regions in California.

1. Explain and use the coordinate grid system of latitude and longitude to determine the absolute locations of places in California and on Earth.

2. Distinguish between the North and South Poles; the equator and the prime meridian; the tropics; and the hemispheres, using coordinates to plot locations.

3. Identify the state capital and describe the various regions of California, including how their characteristics and physical environments (e.g., water, landforms, vegetation, climate) affect human activity.

4. Identify the locations of the Pacific Ocean, rivers, valleys, and mountain passes and explain their effects on the growth of towns.

5. Use maps, charts, and pictures to describe how communities in California vary in land use, vegetation, wildlife, climate, population density, architecture, services, and transportation.

4.2 Students describe the social, political, cultural, and economic life and interactions among people of California from the pre-Columbian societies to the Spanish mission and Mexican rancho periods.

1. Discuss the major nations of California Indians, including their geographic distribution, economic activities, legends, and religious beliefs; and describe how they depended on, adapted to, and modified the physical environment by cultivation of land and use of sea resources.

2. identify the early land and sea routes to, and European settlements in, California with a focus on the exploration of the North Pacific (e.g., by Captain James Cook, Vitus Bering, Juan Cabrillo), noting especially the importance of mountains, deserts, ocean currents, and wind patterns.

3. Describe the Spanish exploration and colonization of California, including the relationships among soldiers, missionaries, and Indians (e.g., Juan Crespi, Junipero Serra, Gaspar de Portola).

4. Describe the mapping of, geographic basis of, and economic factors in the placement and function of the Spanish missions; and understand how the mission system expanded the influence of Spain and Catholicism throughout New Spain and Latin America.

5. Describe the daily lives of the people, native and nonnative, who occupied the presidios, missions, ranchos, and pueblos.

6. Discuss the role of the Franciscans in changing the economy of California from a hunter-gatherer economy to an agricultural economy.

7. Describe the effects of the Mexican War for Independence on Alta California, including its effects on the territorial boundaries of North America.

8. Discuss the period of Mexican rule in California and its attributes, including land grants, secularization of the missions, and the rise of the rancho economy.

4.3 Students explain the economic, social, and political life in California from the establishment of the Bear Flag Republic through the Mexican-American War, the Gold Rush, and the granting of statehood.

1. Identify the locations of Mexican settlements in California and those of other settlements, including Fort Ross and Sutter's Fort.

2. Compare how and why people traveled to California and the routes they traveled (e.g., James Beckwourth, John Bidwell, John C. Fremont, Pio Pico).

3. Analyze the effects of the Gold Rush on settlements, daily life, politics, and the physical environment (e.g., using biographies of John Sutter, Mariano Guadalupe Vallejo, Louise Clapp).

4. Study the lives of women who helped build early California (e.g., Biddy Mason).

5. Discuss how California became a state and how its new government differed from those during the Spanish and Mexican periods.

4.4 Students explain how California became an agricultural and industrial power, tracing the transformation of the California economy and its political and cultural development since the 1850s.

1. Understand the story and lasting influence of the Pony Express, Overland Mail Service, Western Union, and the building of the transcontinental railroad, including the contributions of Chinese workers to its construction.

2. Explain how the Gold Rush transformed the economy of California, including the types of products produced and consumed, changes in towns (e.g., Sacramento, San Francisco), and economic conflicts between diverse groups of people.

3. Discuss immigration and migration to California between 1850 and 1900, including the diverse composition of those who came; the countries of origin and their relative locations; and conflicts and accords among the diverse groups (e.g., the 1882 Chinese Exclusion Act).

4. Describe rapid American immigration, internal migration, settlement, and the growth of towns and cities (e.g., Los Angeles).

5. Discuss the effects of the Great Depression, the Dust Bowl, and World War II on California.

6. Describe the development and locations of new industries since the nineteenth century, such as the aerospace industry, electronics industry, large-scale commercial agriculture and irrigation projects, the oil and automobile industries, communications and defense industries, and important trade links with the Pacific Basin.

7. Trace the evolution of California's water system into a network of dams, aqueducts, and reservoirs.

8. Describe the history and development of California's public education system, including universities and community colleges.

9. Analyze the impact of twentieth-century Californians on the nation's artistic and cultural development, including the rise of the entertainment industry (e.g., Louis B. Meyer, Walt Disney, John Steinbeck, Ansel Adams, Dorothea Lange, John Wayne).

4.5 Students understand the structures, functions, and powers of the local, state, and federal governments as described in the U.S. Constitution.

1. Discuss what the U.S. Constitution is and why it is important (i.e., a written document that defines the structure and purpose of the U.S. government and describes the shared powers of federal, state, and local governments).

2. Understand the purpose of the California Constitution, its key principles, and its relationship to the U.S. Constitution.

3. Describe the similarities (e.g., written documents, rule of law, consent of the governed, three separate branches) and differences (e.g., scope of jurisdiction, limits on government powers, use of the military) among federal, state, and local governments.

4. Explain the structures and functions of state governments, including the roles and responsibilities of their elected officials.

5. Describe the components of California's governance structure (e.g., cities and towns, Indian rancherias and reservations, counties, school districts).

Historical and Social Sciences Analysis Skills

In addition to the standards, students demonstrate the following intellectual, reasoning, reflection, and research skills:

Chronological and Spatial Thinking

1. Students place key events and people of the historical era they are studying in a chronological sequence and within a spatial context; they interpret time lines.
2. Students correctly apply terms related to time, including *past, present, future, decade, century,* and *generation*.
3. Students explain how the present is connected to the past, identifying both similarities and differences between the two, and how some things change over time and some things stay the same.
4. Students use map and globe skills to determine the absolute locations of places and interpret information available through a map's or globe's legend, scale, and symbolic representations.
5. Students judge the significance of the relative location of a place (e.g., proximity to a harbor, on trade routes) and analyze how relative advantages or disadvantages can change over time.

Research, Evidence, and Point of View

1. Students differentiate between primary and secondary sources.
2. Students pose relevant questions about events they encounter in historical documents, eyewitness accounts, oral histories, letters, diaries, artifacts, photographs, maps, artworks, and architecture.
3. Students distinguish fact from fiction by comparing documentary sources on historical figures and events with fictionalized characters and events.

Historical Interpretation

1. Students summarize the key events of the era they are studying and explain the historical contexts of those events.
2. Students identify the human and physical characteristics of the places they are studying and explain how those features form the unique character of those places.
3. Students identify and interpret the multiple causes and effects of historical events.
4. Students conduct cost-benefit analyses of historical and current events.